The Living Savior

VOLUME 8

FAMILY
BIBLE
LIBRARY

V. Gilbert Beers, Ph.D.,Th.D.

THE SOUTHWESTERN COMPANY
Nashville, Tennessee

THE PAINTING ON THE OPPOSITE PAGE
by Loran Raymond Jones
shows the risen Jesus talking with Mary Magdalene.
Jesus had risen from the dead and had broken the bonds
of death for all who follow Him. Through the risen Jesus,
His followers have a new hope and a new life—
another chance to live for God.

What's in this volume

Copyright © 1971 by THE SOUTHWESTERN COMPANY, Nashville, Tennessee
Library of Congress Catalog Card No. 71-155623
Printed in the United States of America
R.R.D.

The story so far…

When God created man and put him into the Garden of Eden, He wanted man to live a godly life. But Adam and Eve, the first man and woman, listened instead to Satan.

Men kept on sinning, obeying Satan instead of God. By the time of Noah, they were very wicked. So God destroyed all people except Noah and his family.

Noah's descendants were no better than his ancestors. By the time of Abraham, almost all of the people were very bad again.

But God made a promise to Abraham that he would become the father of a great nation—a people chosen by God. Abraham's son Isaac and his grandson Jacob had the same promise.

God's promise was fulfilled in Jacob's children, or descendants. Jacob moved to Egypt when his son Joseph became governor. But when Joseph died, all the descendants of Jacob stayed in Egypt. There they lived for almost four hundred years until a new Pharaoh made them become slaves.

The descendants of Jacob, or Israel as he was called later, were finally led from Egypt by Moses. For forty years, they lived in the wilderness and ate manna which God sent to them.

At last, the people of Israel went into a land which God had promised them. For three hundred years, they lived under God's rule, led by judges who took orders from God.

But when the last of the judges, Samuel, became old, the people of Israel demanded a king so they could be like other nations. Saul was appointed and became Israel's first king.

But Saul did not obey God. When he died, David took his place. David was a good warrior and kept other nations from taking

Israel captive. He tried to please God more than Saul had done when he was king.

David's son, Solomon, lived a rich life as king, taxing his people heavily. He married many foreign wives and let them build pagan altars. People began to turn away from God.

When Solomon died, his son Rehoboam would not listen to the advice of his older men. He wanted to live like his father. But the people rebelled and the nation was split in two.

From that time on, most of the kings of Israel and Judah, the two parts of the divided nation, were bad. The nation became weaker and weaker, until it was finally captured and the people taken away.

When some of the people did come back, the nation was again captured by the Greeks, then later by the Romans. The people by this time cried out for the Messiah to come and rebuild their kingdom.

So Jesus was born in "the fullness of time." The Messiah came to the people who prayed so earnestly for Him. But they did not recognize Him when He came. They expected a warrior who would free them from the Romans. Instead, Jesus came preaching and healing and teaching about God.

Jesus did many miracles to show people that He was God's Son. He even raised dead people back to life. But many people could not accept Him as God's Son, the Messiah, for they expected a king over their nation, not a spiritual king. The religious leaders even hated Jesus, for He did not keep the foolish rules they had made. He thought it was more important to do what pleased God. As more and more people turned against Jesus, He began teaching in parables. Those who wanted to believe in Him would understand some of the hidden meaning. Others would hear only an interesting story.

Blind Bartimaeus

Jesus heals Blind Bartimaeus

"Money for the blind!" Blind Bartimaeus called whenever he heard footsteps on the road. "Money for the blind!"

People often dropped a coin for Blind Bartimaeus. Some even stopped to talk with him. He heard many stories of faraway places. Some told of the Roman army. Others spoke of the great feast days

in Jerusalem. Once in awhile, some spoke of a Teacher far away in Galilee who did great miracles. His name was Jesus.

"He even gave sight to some blind people," they said.

Whenever Blind Bartimaeus heard about Jesus, he longed for the day when He might come on this road to Jericho. If only He could help Blind Bartimaeus see.

Blind Bartimaeus had never seen before. People had tried to tell him about trees and flowers and clouds in the sky. He had often thought what colors might be like. What would red be? Or blue? If only he could see something besides darkness all the time. But Blind Bartimaeus knew he would never see these beautiful things unless . . . unless the Teacher from Galilee would come this way.

"Don't even think about it," some told him. "He will probably never come to Jericho."

But Blind Bartimaeus never stopped praying that someday the Teacher would come. What a wonderful day that would be!

"Thousands crowd around Him," some said. "Even if He came by, you might never get to Him."

Blind Bartimaeus knew this was true. But he still prayed that Jesus might come. He would give anything to see.

One day Blind Bartimaeus was sitting in his place, begging for coins, when he heard the sound of many voices along the road. He stopped begging to listen. The sound was coming closer. It was getting louder. What could it be?

"What's happening?" he asked people who hurried by.

"Jesus is in Jericho," they said. "He's coming this way."

Bartimaeus longed for the day when Jesus would come on his road.

Blind Bartimaeus felt his heart skip a beat. His prayers were answered. Jesus was coming on the very road where he was sitting. He was so excited.

But what if Jesus would pass by and never see him? How could he get Jesus to hear with all that noise?

The sound of the crowd came closer and closer. When it came near Blind Bartimaeus, the beggar began to shout.

"Jesus, Son of David, have mercy on me!" he cried out. It seemed to him that his voice was lost in the crowd. What could he do? He must not miss Jesus now, not when He was so close. It was his only chance to see.

So Blind Bartimaeus began to cry out as loud as he could. "Jesus, have mercy on me! Son of David, help me!"

With all his heart he cried out for Jesus. He felt desperate now. Jesus must hear him.

"Quiet, old beggar," some complained.

But Blind Bartimaeus kept shouting, "Jesus, help me." Another minute would be too late.

Then suddenly the noisy crowd stopped. The people became quiet. "What's happening?" Blind Bartimaeus wondered.

"Bring him here to Me," a kind voice said.

Then voices near to Blind Bartimaeus called to him. "Hurry, Jesus is calling you. He wants you to come to Him."

This was the moment Blind Bartimaeus had waited for so long. He threw off his long mantle and hurried toward the kind voice he had heard.

"What do you want Me to do for you?" the kind voice asked.

"Oh, Master, let me see," Blind Bartimaeus answered. His voice trembled now, for it was a cry of faith. The blind man knew that Jesus was his only hope. And he was begging for mercy now, not coins.

10

"What do you want Me to do for you?" a kind voice asked.

11

The kind voice spoke once more. "Go your way; your faith has made you well," Jesus said.

Suddenly the whole world became different to Blind Bartimaeus. Night became day, darkness melted away into a beautiful light, and he saw a world that was filled with color beyond all his dreams. But the most wonderful thing of all was the kind face looking down in his. It was the face of Jesus.

Jesus smiled, then turned and started down the road again. Bartimaeus gave a parting look at the place where he had sat by the roadside for so many years. Then he picked up his mantle and followed after Jesus. He would never leave the One who had done so much for him.

SOMETHING TO THINK ABOUT

1. Close your eyes for a full minute. How long did it seem? How would it feel to keep your eyes closed for an hour? For a day? How would you feel if you knew you could never open your eyes again? That's the way Blind Bartimaeus felt. The whole world was nothing but darkness.

2. Blind people in Jesus' time could not get a job. There weren't enough jobs for people who could see. Many people in Jesus' country were very poor, even the people who were healthy. So, there wasn't much for a blind person to do but sit by the side of a road and beg for coins. To the misery of being blind, he had to add the shame of becoming a beggar.

3. What do you think Blind Bartimaeus wanted more than anything else in the world? What would you have wanted most of all? But there were no surgeons to operate on blind people and help them see. There were no hospitals or special medicines either.

4. But there was one hope for Blind Bartimaeus. What was it? If you had been Blind Bartimaeus would you have longed for the day when Jesus would come by your road? Would you have believed in Him and trusted Him to heal you?

5. If we believe in Jesus and trust Him as Blind Bartimaeus did, He can help us too. Will you believe in Him and trust Him?

12

The women of Jericho still come to get water at Elisha's Fountain, the main source of water for the city.

The road from Jerusalem to Jericho, along which Blind Bartimaeus sat, was a busy road. The warm climate of Jericho, eight hundred feet below sea level, and the beautiful springs and palm trees, brought winter travelers from the cold hills in which Jerusalem was built, especially when Herod the Great built his winter capital there.

Jericho, one of the oldest cities in the world, was built by a ford of the Jordan River, one of the few places where the river could be crossed. It therefore became a "gateway" for travel from the East.

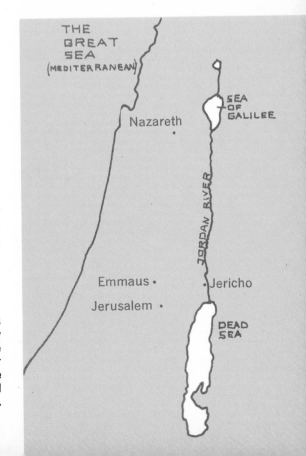

THE GREAT SEA (MEDITERRANEAN)

Nazareth

SEA OF GALILEE

JORDAN RIVER

Emmaus •

Jericho

Jerusalem •

DEAD SEA

A Little Man in a Big Tree

Zacchaeus climbs a tree
to see Jesus

Nobody liked Zacchaeus! Nobody liked him because he was a tax collector.

"Zacchaeus takes more money than he should," some people said.

"Zacchaeus gets richer while we get poorer," said others.

"Those tax collectors are all alike," said some other people. "They work for our enemies, the Romans. They don't care if we have enough to eat."

Everywhere Zacchaeus went he heard people whisper bad things about him. Zacchaeus knew that most of the bad things people said were true, too.

"If only I had a friend," Zacchaeus thought. "I'd rather have a friend than all my money."

But Zacchaeus didn't have a friend. Nobody wanted to be a tax collector's friend, even if he was the richest man in Jericho. Nobody wanted to go to Zacchaeus' house, even if it was the most beautiful house in town.

14

*Zacchaeus ran as fast as he could go,
but he couldn't catch up.*

Zacchaeus was very, very sad. He thought he would never have a friend again.

One day Zacchaeus was walking down a road near Jericho. He heard the people whisper bad things as he went by, just as they always did. But suddenly Zacchaeus heard something else. Someone was shouting.

"Jesus is coming! Jesus is coming!" someone cried out.

People began to run down the road as fast as they could go. Everyone wanted to see Jesus. He was a Friend to all the people.

"Perhaps Jesus would be my Friend, too," Zacchaeus thought. "I must try to see Him."

Zacchaeus ran down the road. He ran as fast as his legs would go. But he couldn't catch up with the other people.

Zacchaeus was very sad when he saw a big crowd of people around Jesus. How would he ever get to see Jesus? How could he ever ask Him to be his Friend? He was so short that he could never see Jesus. Nobody would let a tax collector get inside the crowd.

15

When Jesus looked up at him,
Zacchaeus felt like he wanted to hide.

The crowd moved along the road. Closer and closer to Zacchaeus it came. Zacchaeus stepped off the road to let all the people go by. He sat down in the shade of a big sycamore tree.

Suddenly Zacchaeus had an idea. He jumped up and began to climb the big sycamore tree. Then he slowly climbed out on one of the limbs.

16

Zacchaeus looked this way and that to see Jesus. There were so many people! Where was He?

As the crowd came under the tree, Zacchaeus caught his breath. There was Jesus! He wanted to call to Jesus and ask Him to come to his house for a visit. But Zacchaeus suddenly felt ashamed of all the bad things that he had done. How could he ask Jesus to come to his house? How could he even talk to Jesus? Jesus would not want to be his friend.

Then Jesus stopped. He looked up at the little man in the big tree. Zacchaeus felt like he wanted to hide. The most honored Man in Jericho was looking at the most hated man in Jericho.

"Zacchaeus!" Jesus called to him. Zacchaeus could have fallen out of the tree. How did Jesus know his name?

"Come down from that tree," Jesus said. "I'm going to your house today."

Zacchaeus could hardly believe his ears. But he lost no time coming down from the sycamore tree.

That day, Zacchaeus heard many things about God and Heaven. He heard about the wonderful life that Jesus could give. The more Zacchaeus listened, the more he wanted that life.

"Lord, I'm going to give half of everything I own to the poor," Zacchaeus said at last. "If I've cheated anyone, I'll give that person four times as much as I've taken."

Jesus was very happy to hear what Zacchaeus said. He knew this was not easy for a tax collector to do.

"Today salvation has come to this house," said Jesus.

Then Jesus spoke some wonderful words. "The Son of Man has come to seek and to save the lost," He said.

Zacchaeus knew that he was one of those who had been lost. How different his life would be now that Jesus had found him! How different it would be now that Jesus was his Friend!

WHAT WAS THE SYCAMORE TREE?

The sycamore tree (sometimes spelled sycomore) is not the same as the tree we know by that name. It is one kind of fig tree in Bible lands.

Small round figs about an inch long grow on the sycamore tree. The figs do not taste very good.

In Bible times people punched a hole in one end of each fig to make it get ripe faster. Amos, the prophet, sometimes did this kind of work (Amos 7: 14).

The sycamore tree sometimes grows as high as forty or fifty feet. It has a large trunk. Sometimes the roots stand out of the ground for several feet.

The wood of the sycamore tree was valuable in ancient times. Egyptians made mummy cases and wood utensils from it.

The sycamore tree cannot grow in high places. It cannot stand the cold air or frost. Usually it is found in warmer places. Sycamore trees grow easily around the warm climate of Jericho, for Jericho is hundreds of feet below sea level.

There were probably many of these sycamore trees in Bible lands when Jesus lived. But like many of the trees of that land, they have been cut or destroyed, but not replaced until recent years.

The sycamore tree was large enough for Zacchaeus to climb on its branches.

A large sycamore tree grows in the city of Jericho today. It is probably much like the tree Zacchaeus climbed to see Jesus.

Matthew 21: 1-11, 14-17; Mark 11: 1-11; Luke 19: 28-44;
John 11: 55—12: 1, 12-19

Onward to Jerusalem

Jesus' triumphal entry into Jerusalem

"Do you see that village over there?" Jesus asked two of His disciples. "I want you to go over there." The disciples nodded. Whatever Jesus wanted, they would do it for Him.

"You will find a donkey tied to a fence," Jesus said. "Untie it and bring it to Me. If anyone asks what you are doing, tell them the Lord needs this donkey and will bring it back soon."

The two disciples hurried away. They didn't understand it all, but they knew that Jesus never made a mistake.

It all happened the way Jesus said it would. There was the young donkey, so young no one had sat on it before. It was tied at the very place Jesus said it would be.

When the two disciples began to untie the donkey, the owner and a friend ran up to them.

"What are you doing?" the owner asked.

The two disciples wondered if the owner would be angry. Would he let them take the donkey? Jesus said he would.

"The Lord needs this donkey," the two disciples said. "He will bring it back soon."

20

"What are you doing?"
some men cried out.

The owner smiled. "Of course you may take the donkey and let Him use it," he said.

By the time the two disciples came back, a big crowd of people had gathered around Jesus. Many were people Jesus had healed. Some had been blind. Others had been sick with leprosy. Others had been filled with demons. But all of them were well now. They would never forget what He had done for them.

"Israel needs a leader like Jesus," they thought. "If only we could make Him our King."

People living in Jerusalem had heard that Jesus was nearby. They came to join the crowd, too. Even some of the religious leaders came out to see what was happening.

The people were getting more and more excited. All over the crowd they whispered, "Let's make Jesus our King."

"Perhaps this is the time for Jesus to become King of Israel," the disciples thought. "The Scriptures say that the King will come riding on a donkey."

21

But no one had kingly robes for Jesus. There was no crown to put on His head. So some of the disciples threw their cloaks on the donkey's back and helped Jesus get up on it.

Suddenly someone shouted, "Hosanna! Blessed be He who comes in the name of the Lord!"

"Blessed be the kingdom of our father David that is coming!" others cried out. "Hosanna in the highest."

Soon there was a great chorus of voices, shouting praises to the new King. Then someone began to lead the donkey down the Mount of Olives. The Triumphal Entry into Jerusalem had begun.

People came from everywhere to see what was happening. "What is all the excitement?" they asked.

"It's the Prophet Jesus," some answered. "He's going to Jerusalem to be made King of Israel."

"A new King for Israel?" the people thought. "Perhaps He will free us from the Romans." So more and more joined in the shouting, happy procession.

In the excitement, many threw their cloaks on the ground before Jesus. Others cut leafy branches in the fields and spread them in the road for the donkey to walk on. Even the children began to shout with joy because their Friend was causing so much happiness.

But not everyone was happy. Some of the leaders had come out to see what was happening. They did not want Jesus to become King. They might lose their jobs!

"Teacher, scold those disciples of Yours for doing this," the leaders said angrily.

Jesus looked at them sadly. "If I stop them, the stones will begin to cry out," He said. Nothing could stop this from taking place, for the Scriptures had said it would happen.

What a procession went into Jerusalem! Never had there been anything like it. But never had there been a King like Jesus.

The people all shouted praises to Jesus as He rode into Jerusalem.

THE TRIUMPHAL ENTRY

Jesus began His triumphal entry into Jerusalem somewhere between
Bethany and Bethphage. He rode past the Garden of Gethsemane,
or through it, then down the Kidron Valley, and up into
Jerusalem through the Golden Gate.

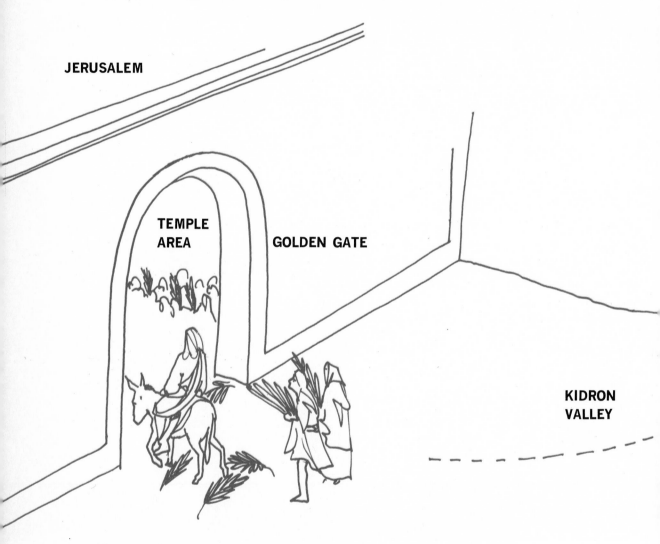

The people who crowded around Jesus thought that He was going to make
Himself King of Israel. They were happy, for they thought He would help
them get the Romans out of their land. That was what the people expected
from the Messiah. But Jesus would disappoint the people and turn many against
Him by doing what the Messiah was supposed to do—to die for the sin of His
people and make possible a way to God. He would become King over all kings
of the earth, but the people did not know that then.

24

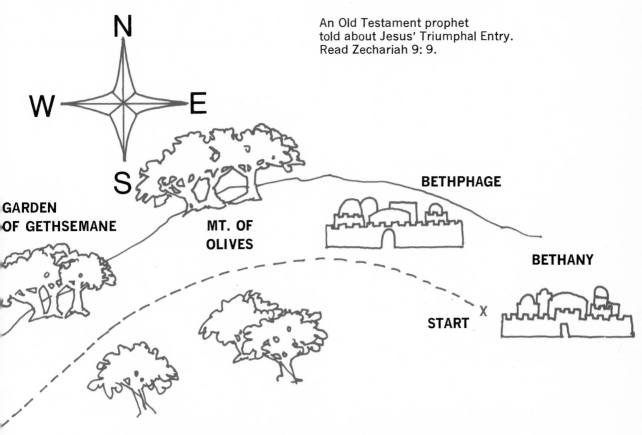

An Old Testament prophet told about Jesus' Triumphal Entry. Read Zechariah 9: 9.

BETHPHAGE

GARDEN OF GETHSEMANE

MT. OF OLIVES

BETHANY

START

Some call the Sunday before Easter "Palm Sunday," remembering the day when Jesus rode into Jerusalem. Some of the people in the crowd cut palm branches and waved them in the air. See John 12: 13.

A Story of Two Sons

Parable of two sons

One day Jesus told the Pharisees a story about themselves.

A father came to one of his two sons to ask for help. "Will you work in our vineyard today?" the father asked.

The son had made plans for the day. He wanted to have fun with his friends.

"No, I won't," the son answered. Then he walked off and left his father standing with a surprised look on his face.

The father was very sorry that his son had refused to help. Perhaps his other son would work with him in the vineyard.

"Of course," the other son answered. "I'll be glad to help in the vineyard."

The father was happy that one son was willing to help. So he went to get some tools ready.

While he was gone, both sons began to think about what they had said. The first son felt sorry that he had been so unkind. So he told his friends that he could not go with them. He would stay and help his father.

But the other son began thinking of all the fun he could have instead of working. So while his father was gone, he slipped away to find his friends.

*The father was so glad that one son
had helped him in the vineyard.*

When the father came back with the tools, he found the first son waiting for him. "I'm sorry for what I said, Father," the first son said. "I'll help you today."

"I'm so glad," answered the father. "But where is your brother?"

The first son pointed toward the road. "I think he decided not to help us," he said. "He went away with his friends."

Jesus turned to the Pharisees. "Now which of these two sons really obeyed his father and did what the father wanted?" He asked.

There was only one answer. "The first son, of course," they said. "Because he finally did what his father wanted."

Jesus looked at the Pharisees sternly. "I tell you," He said, "that the tax collectors and bad people will get to Heaven before you do."

The Pharisees gasped. How could Jesus say such a thing? They had always lived good lives. But the tax collectors and bad people hadn't.

"You've been telling your Father in Heaven that you want to work for Him," said Jesus, "but when John the Baptist came to show you God's work, you refused to do it."

Jesus was telling the Pharisees that they were like the second son. They had said, "Yes, we will do Your work." But then they went off with their friends.

"But some of the tax collectors and bad people listened to John," said Jesus.

They were like the first son. They had said "no" to God at first, but they were sorry and asked Him to forgive them. Then they went to do His work.

The Pharisees did not like to hear Jesus put tax collectors and bad people before them. It made them angry to think that those people would go to Heaven before them. But Jesus spoke the truth and often the truth hurts.

SOMETHING TO THINK ABOUT

1. Which son pleased his father more—the son who said he would help, but didn't, or the son who said he would not, but did?
2. Jesus was talking about the Pharisees, who said they would serve God, but then did not do His work. He was saying that the bad people who repented from their bad ways and began to work for God pleased Him much more than the Pharisees.

BIBLE-TIME VINEYARDS

One of the most important plants in Bible times was the grape vine. From it people had grapes to eat, grape juice, grape honey, wine, grape sugar, and raisins. Sugar cane was not grown in Bible lands, so people did not have the white sugar or brown sugar which we use today. They had to use grape sugar or grape honey to sweeten their foods, unless someone was fortunate enough to find some wild honey. Raisins were very important to travelers and soldiers for they were easy to carry and did not spoil.

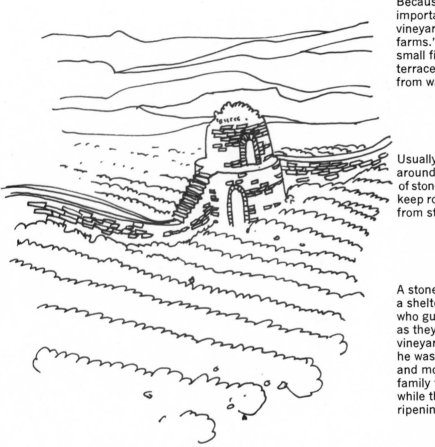

Because grapes were so important, people planted vineyards, or "grape farms." A vineyard was a small field with stone terraces to keep the soil from washing away.

Usually a wall was built around the vineyard, made of stones or thorn bushes, to keep robbers and animals from stealing the grapes.

A stone tower was built as a shelter for the watchman who guarded the grapes as they ripened. If a vineyard owner was poor, he was his own watchman, and moved his entire family to the watchtower while the grapes were ripening.

Vineyards required much work. The ground had to be hoed to make it soft so water did not run off. Other plants and roots had to be cut out constantly. Vines had to be pruned so more strength would go to the grapes, not to the vines. But when harvest time came in the summer, the happy owner thought it was worth all the hard work.

29

Caesar or God?

The leaders try to trap Jesus again

The leaders in the Temple were desperate. Each day, Jesus attracted more and more attention. Each day, more people came to hear Him teach.

If this kept up, the people would certainly make Him the King of Israel. Then the leaders would not rule over the people. They would have to give up their jobs, for they knew Jesus did not like the way they were doing things.

Hardly an hour passed without someone trying to find a way to trap Jesus. If only He would say something wrong. But He didn't. So the leaders tried again and again to get Him to say something wrong.

One day a new trap was set. The Pharisees sent their followers to trick Jesus. Along with them went some other leaders, called Herodians.

"Teacher," they said. "We know that you are true, and teach the way of God truthfully. You do not care about the jobs that men hold."

They would try flattery at first. Perhaps they could catch Jesus off guard if they paid Him compliments.

30

The leaders had set a trap for Jesus and they hoped He would say the wrong things.

But Jesus was watching for their traps now. He listened carefully as they talked.

"What do you think?" they asked. "Is it lawful to pay taxes to Caesar, or not?"

It was a carefully planned trap. If Jesus said it was lawful to pay taxes, the people would turn against him, for they hated to pay taxes to the Romans. But if He said it was not lawful, the leaders would have the Romans arrest Jesus for teaching against them.

Again, it looked as if the leaders had trapped Jesus. There was no answer that could get Him out of this.

31

"Show me a coin," Jesus said.

"Why are you trying to trick Me like this?" Jesus asked them. "Show Me the coin which people use to pay the tax."

Quickly someone reached into a bag and brought the coin to show to Jesus.

Jesus turned the coin over and over in His hands. The people became very quiet as He studied it.

32

"He's stalling for time," someone whispered.

"Shhh," someone else whispered back. "No one has ever caught Jesus in a trap before. They won't catch Him this time, you'll see."

Jesus looked at the people who had tried to catch Him. "Whose picture is on this coin?" He asked.

Quickly they all spoke up, like children trying to answer first on a quiz. "Caesar's!" they said.

Jesus gave the coin back to its owner. Then He turned to the people who had tried to trap Him. "Then give Caesar what belongs to Caesar and give God what belongs to God."

The people were all astonished at this answer. Jesus had caught the leaders in the trap they had set for Him. They had been giving Caesar what belonged to him, but they had not been giving God what He wanted.

"I told you they wouldn't trap Jesus," the person who had spoken to his friend whispered.

"Yes," said the other man. "He is certainly a great Prophet, isn't He? Perhaps He is God's Son, just as He says."

SOMETHING TO THINK ABOUT

1. Why were the Pharisees trying to trick Jesus? Why did they want to turn the people against Him?
2. If Jesus had said that people should pay taxes to their enemies, would the people have liked Him? They would probably all become angry with Jesus, for they hated their enemies, the Romans.
3. But if Jesus had said that they should not pay their taxes, what would the Pharisees have done? Would they have told the Romans so Jesus would get into trouble? That was their plan.
4. Do you think there are people today who would like to make Jesus look foolish? Are there some who want to turn others against Him?
5. What did some of the people learn about Jesus? Who is He? If Jesus is God's Son, then we should obey Him and give our lives to Him, shouldn't we?

TAXES IN JESUS' TIME

Jesus' neighbors were very poor. Many of them did not have a job. Some of them had almost nothing. A man who became blind or crippled was almost sure to become a beggar, for nobody would hire him. It was too easy to get healthy people to work.

When a man was fortunate enough to get any kind of job, he earned about sixteen cents for a full day of hard work, from sunrise to sunset. He didn't complain either, for he knew that it might be a few days before he could find another job. People were hired for a day at a time, not for a long period of time as they are today. Since people were so poor, taxes became an extra burden. People may pay more taxes today than they did in Jesus' time, but they have much more left. Nobody then could afford such beautiful homes, clothes, good food, or luxuries. People hated taxes because they made them even poorer than they were.

TEMPLE TAXES

What would you think if your church made you pay taxes? The Temple made Jesus and His neighbors pay. Every male Jew, twenty years or older, had to pay a half shekel, about thirty-two cents, which was two days' wages, to the Temple treasury each year. This was not an offering, but a tax.

With this money, the religious leaders bought animals to sacrifice, paid their own living expenses, and other expenses necessary to keep up the Temple.

Since the Temple was God's house, God's Son should not have had to pay this tax. But He did pay it to keep from starting trouble (Matthew 17: 24-27). Jesus had Peter catch a fish in which there was a coin, a shekel, enough for Jesus' tax, as well as Peter's.

The half-shekel was often used to pay the Temple tax for one man. The stater, which was worth the same as a shekel, was probably the coin Peter found in the fish's mouth. It was enough to pay his tax and Jesus'. The shekel, shown here, was also used to pay for two persons.

Both the shekel and half-shekel had a cup on the front, which was a cup of manna. The plant on the back, with three buds or fruits, was probably Aaron's rod which budded like a plant.

FRONT   **BACK**

THE HALF SHEKEL

FRONT   **BACK**

THE SHEKEL

FRONT

BACK

THE STATER, WORTH A SHEKEL

CAESAR'S TAXES

While Jesus lived on earth, Israel was part of the Roman Empire. Rome ruled over Israel. Caesar, the emperor, was the man over all the empire. Caesar was more powerful than a president or prime minister. He was more powerful than a dictator. Caesar was like a god, having the power of life and death over his people. He expected his people to think of him as a god, too.

BACK

**THE
TRIBUTE
COIN
(DENARIUS)**

FRONT

Since Israel was part of the Roman Empire, Israel and her people paid taxes to Rome. Naturally, the people of Israel hated to pay taxes to a foreign government. But they hated the taxes more because the Romans were Gentiles, and Gentiles were "pagan dogs."

There were two kinds of taxes paid to Rome (see volume 6, pages 156, 157). One was the Imperial Tax, paid to Rome's officers. It was this tax which Jesus spoke of when He said, "Give to Caesar what belongs to Caesar" (Matthew 22: 15-22). The other tax was a customs tax, paid at houses of customs along important roads. It was a tax on goods which people carried along the road. The publican or tax collector received this tax. He was usually a Jew who bought this office from Rome. He could charge as much above the tax as he wanted and keep the difference for himself. The publican was hated bitterly, for he often charged far more than the person should pay. This made him rich and his neighbor poor.

There were bitter feelings in the land about these taxes. If the leaders could get Jesus to take a stand against the taxes, they could get Rome to arrest Him. If He took a stand for them, the people would hate Him. But Jesus gave a perfect answer which silenced His enemies.

The Imperial Tax coin was the denarius, or tribute penny. On its face was the image or picture of Caesar.

35

The Little Gift
That Was Very Big

The widow's gift

"Look at the money that rich man put in the offering box," one of the disciples said.

"And look how much the man behind him has in his hand," said another.

Jesus did look. But He said nothing.

The disciples stood with Jesus for some time, watching people come into the treasury of the Temple, where the offering box was kept. They watched the people put in their gifts to help with God's work.

"Isn't it wonderful to see how much money some of those people are giving?" some of the disciples asked. "They're doing so much for God's work."

"Yes," said others. "But look how little some of the others give. They're certainly not helping God's work very much!"

Jesus watched the people give their small gifts and their big gifts. But still He said nothing.

"Why doesn't Jesus say something about those gifts?" one of the disciples whispered.

36

The poor widow had only one small coin to give.
But it was more than the rich men's gold.

"I don't know," said another. "Perhaps He will scold some of those people who don't give very much. He certainly should."

While the disciples talked, a poor widow lady came into the Temple treasury. Slowly she walked up to the offering box. Then she reached into a bag and took out a small coin. She slipped the small coin into the offering box and hurried on her way.

"Shame on her!" one of the disciples whispered. "Did you see what she gave? That coin isn't worth much at all. The man ahead of her gave a thousand times more than she did."

"No," said Jesus. "She gave more than all the people who came in here today."

The disciples turned to look at Jesus. How surprised they were to hear Him say that. The woman had given almost nothing. Many others had given big offerings. What did Jesus mean?

"I tell you that this poor widow put in more than all the other people," Jesus said again.

"What do you mean, Lord?" the disciples asked.

Then Jesus taught the disciples a lesson they would never forget. "When all those other people gave, they still had much more left at home. They gave only a small part of their money for God's work. But the poor widow gave her last coin. That was all the money she had. But she gave it all to God's work. Now tell me which one gave the most?"

The disciples looked down at the floor. They felt so ashamed. That little coin the widow gave looked so big now. And the big gold coins the rich people gave looked so small.

"Jesus is right," one of the disciples whispered. "It's not how much we give that counts. It's how we give it."

What a lesson to learn! God loves that dime which some boy or girl wants to give to Him. He loves it more than the thousand dollars some rich man feels he has to give.

38

THE WIDOW'S GIFT

THE GIFT

The mite, or lepton, which the widow gave was one of the smallest coins in use during the time of Jesus. It was worth only a half of a cent. Her two mites were worth about a penny.

Front

Back

THE OFFERING CONTAINER

In the Court of Women, which was also known as The Treasury of the Temple, there were thirteen trumpet-shaped boxes in which people put their offerings. The neck of each chest was narrow, so that money put into the chest could not be taken out again through the neck.

THE TREASURY, WHERE SHE GAVE IT

The widow was in The Women's Court, or Treasury, of the Temple when she gave her two mites. The Women's Court was the last court of the Temple into which women could go (see volume 6, pages 12 and 13 for a description of this court and a picture of the Temple). To this court all devoted people came with their offerings and deposited them in one of the offering chests near the pillars of the room. It was probably in this same room where Anna and Simeon had seen the baby Jesus and had told Mary that He was the Messiah (Luke 2: 21-38. See volume 6, pages 40-45). Here also, Jesus forgave the sinful woman (John 7: 53—8: 11. See volume 6, pages 44-45).

Ten Talents

Parable of the talents

Jesus knew that He would soon leave the earth to go back to His home in Heaven. But what would His disciples do while He was away? Jesus wanted every one of His followers to use time and talents well. One day He told His disciples a story so they would understand what they should do about their talents.

A certain merchant planned a long trip to a far country. Before he left, he called three of his best servants to him to tell them what to do while he was gone.

"I must go away for awhile," he told his servants. "But I will leave you in charge of my money while I am gone."

To his best servant, the merchant gave five talents, or about a hundred and fifty thousand dollars in gold. To another servant he gave two talents, about sixty thousand dollars. To a third, he gave one talent, about thirty thousand dollars.

"Use these talents wisely," the merchant told the men. Then he went away on his trip.

The man with the five talents started to work right away. He bought and sold. He worked and traded.

"I must work hard for my master," he thought. "He has trusted me with much money."

40

*The lazy servant buried his talent one night
while the city slept.*

The man with the two talents went to work just as quickly as
the one with five talents. He worked and traded, bought and sold,
too.

"I will do everything I can for my master," he thought. "He
trusted me with his money. I must not fail him."

But the servant with one talent went out in his yard one night
while the city slept. Quietly he dug a hole and buried his one talent
of gold. During the days that followed, he often saw the other two
servants working. Early in the morning he watched them go to the
marketplace. Late at night he saw them come home.

"Foolish fellows," he said to himself. "Why should I work so
hard for someone else? I'll use this time to have fun and do things
I've always wanted to do."

So the third servant wasted all his time. One day another servant knocked at his door.

"The master has returned," he said breathlessly. "He wants you and the other two servants to come. Hurry. He's waiting for you right now!"

The servant with one talent was in no hurry. He finished what he was doing, then went out to his yard. Slowly he dug up the talent of gold and took it to his master. The other two servants were already with the master when he came in. He listened to hear what they would say.

The servant with five talents walked happily toward his master. He held a large box of gold. There were nine more boxes standing on the floor beside him.

"Master," he said, "you gave me five talents of gold. I've worked hard with it, for I wanted to please you. Now I have ten talents for you."

The master was very pleased with this servant. He had doubled his money while he was away.

"Well done!" said the master. "You've been very faithful with my money. Now I know I can trust you. I'll put you in charge of much more than ten talents."

The servant was so happy. This was the best reward he could have.

The second servant came forward now. He held a large box of gold, too. There were three more boxes beside him.

"You gave me two talents of gold," the servant told his master. "I, too, have worked very hard. Now I have four talents for you."

The master was just as pleased with the second servant as he was with the first. "Good," he said. "You have been very faithful, too. Because I know I can trust you, I'll put you in charge of a large amount of money, too."

The second servant was very happy that the master would trust him with so much. He would certainly work hard for him.

42

"Well done!"
the master said to his faithful servant.

By now the third servant had come to the master. He carried a box of gold. But he had nothing else with him.

"Master," he said, "I know what kind of person you are. You want other people to do your work for you. Well, I didn't do it! Here is the talent you gave me. Take it back."

The merchant was angry to think that this fellow had done nothing while he was gone. He had wasted his time. He had done nothing with the master's money.

"You lazy, wicked man," the master said. "If you didn't want to work with the money, you could at least have taken it to the bankers and let them use it so I would have interest on it."

The master turned to some men near him. "Take the gold from that lazy servant and give it to the fellow with ten talents," he ordered. "Then throw this worthless man out."

So two servants went out to serve their master with great power and glory. But the third went out empty-handed and alone.

The disciples learned an important lesson from this story. Jesus wants us to use our time, our talents, and our treasure. We must use them—or lose them!

The master was angry with the lazy fellow who had done nothing.

SOMETHING TO THINK ABOUT

1. What does this story teach about faithfulness? Which servants were faithful to their master? Which was not faithful to his master?

2. How would you have felt if you had been the master? Would you have been pleased with the lazy servant's work? Why not? Would you have done anything different from that which the master did?

3. Jesus was teaching about Himself, our Lord and Master, leaving to go back to Heaven. What "talents" has He left with us? What do you think God has given to you to use?

4. God has allowed some people to make much money. Others have great abilities, others have time to use for Him.

5. What are some things we can do with our time, our treasure, and our talents? Make a list of all the things which you think would please God. Which of these can you do? Which can you do this next week?

6. How can you be faithful with your time, treasure, and talents? Are you faithful if you waste your time? What if you spend your money for foolish things? Will God think you are faithful if you have ability to do certain things, but never practice or develop your ability? Will He be pleased if you use your ability for ungodly things?

7. Romans 12: 6 tells us that we each have different talents, but that God wants us to use whatever we have. Find out what you can do for God. Then start doing it cheerfully. This was Paul's advice to Timothy in I Timothy 4: 14.

BIBLE-TIME STEWARDS

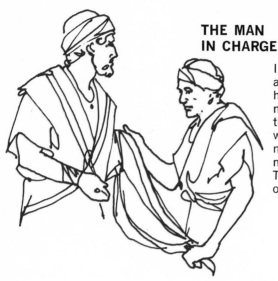

THE MAN IN CHARGE

In Jesus' time, a steward was a man placed in charge of a household. While most of Jesus' neighbors were too poor to pay their own way, there were a few who had so much money and so many possessions that they needed a man to take care of them. The steward might be a hired man, or he might be a slave.

THE MAN WHO PAID THE WORKERS

The steward paid the workers at the end of a working day. Men were hired to work by the day, not by the week or month. At the close of the day, the steward paid each man the day's wage, usually about sixteen cents. The wage was paid with a denarius or a drachma. Each coin was worth the same, about sixteen cents.

The steward was trusted with the master's property, either a part of it or all of it. He was usually over the people, such as servants and workmen, as well as the money and household. Often, the steward was even in charge of educating the master's children. He was very important to his master, for the master had given much for him to care for.

46

STORIES ABOUT STEWARDS

People in Jesus' time knew about stewards, for Jesus mentioned them often in His teaching. Joanna, the wife of Herod's steward, Chuzas, followed Jesus and helped to care for Him.
See Luke 8: 3.

THE LABORERS IN THE VINEYARD

In the story of the laborers in the vineyard, the steward paid the workmen at the end of the day.
Matthew 20: 1-16.

THE UNJUST STEWARD

One steward misused his master's money. When the master heard about it, he called the steward and demanded an accounting of his money. Then he made his steward quit.
Luke 16: 1-13.

THE WICKED HUSBANDMEN

When a vineyard owner left his vineyard in charge of tenants, who may have been stewards or tenant farmers, he was surprised to find that they beat his servants who came to collect his rightful part. Then they killed his son and tried to take the vineyard. Jesus told this parable to illustrate His death.
Matthew 21: 33-46.

The Bible tells us to be good stewards while Jesus is away.
I Peter 4: 10; I Corinthians 4: 1, 2.
This was the reason for the story of the good and bad stewards, to tell us what He expects. He wants us to use our time, talents, and treasures wisely.

47

*Martha served the dinner
as she always did
for Jesus.*

Mary's Gift

Mary pours ointment on Jesus

It was the last visit Jesus would ever make with His friends at Bethany. They had all come to dinner at the house of Simon, whom Jesus had healed of leprosy.

Lazarus, whom Jesus had raised from the dead, was there. So were his sisters Mary and Martha. As usual, Mary stayed close to Jesus, listening to the wonderful words He spoke. Of course, Martha served the dinner. She always liked to keep herself busy with those things.

But it was a sad dinner that day, for Jesus told His disciples and close friends how He would be killed by the Pharisees. It would

not be long now before He would be crucified outside a city gate of Jerusalem. His friends must understand that this was His last meal with them.

Mary was sad when she heard what Jesus said. Never again would she be able to listen to the wonderful things He told about Heaven.

Suddenly Mary had an idea. She quietly left the room and went to her home. In a few moments she came back with a beautiful stone jar.

49

Without saying a word, Mary walked to Jesus, who was still sitting at the table talking with His friends. Before anyone knew what was happening, Mary began to pour ointment from the jar onto Jesus' head. Then all eyes turned toward her as the sweet smell of the ointment filled the room.

Everyone recognized the smell. It was nard, or spikenard—a very expensive ointment imported from lands far away. Everyone gasped when they saw Mary empty the entire jar on Jesus. It would take a man almost a year to earn enough money to buy that much of the costly ointment. She had shown great honor to Jesus by doing this.

Suddenly there was a stir in the room. Judas Iscariot, the disciples' treasurer stood up. He was angry. "This is a waste of money," he complained. "This ointment could have been sold and the money given to the poor."

But Jesus knew what was in Judas' heart. He wasn't really interested in the poor. He was planning how to betray his Master to His enemies. He wanted more money in the disciples' moneybag when he turned traitor and kept it.

"Don't bother Mary," Jesus told him. "She has done something very beautiful. You will always have poor people with you, but you won't always have Me."

Then Jesus turned to look at Mary. Her eyes were filled with tears.

"Mary has poured this ointment on Me to prepare Me for burial," Jesus said. "Wherever the Gospel is preached, people will always remember what she has done."

Jesus was right. Many hundreds of sermons and Bible stories have been told about Mary's gift. People will never forget what Mary did. It was the best she had, and she gave it to the Person she loved most.

50

*It was a strange gift,
but it was the best that Mary had.*

SOMETHING TO THINK ABOUT

1. People today would not appreciate having a jar of ointment poured on their heads. But in Jesus' time, it was a great honor for someone to do this. Mary's gift was very special.

2. What special gifts can you give to Jesus to show Him that you love Him? Why not make a list, then try to give Him one gift each day this week?

WHAT THE OLD TESTAMENT
SAID ABOUT JESUS

Simeon and Anna knew much about the Baby they saw, for they had read many things about Jesus in the Old Testament, the only part of the Bible they had at that time. These prophecies, or things the prophets told many years before they happened, all came true. Here are some of the prophecies from the Old Testament and the places in the New Testament where they came true. Look them up in your Bible.

Jesus would be born in Bethlehem
Micah 5: 2   Matthew 2: 1, 4-6

Jesus would live for awhile in Egypt
Hosea 11: 1   Matthew 2: 14, 15

The children of Bethlehem would be killed
which would cause great sorrow
Jermiah 31: 15   Matthew 2: 16-18

Jesus would live in Galilee
Isaiah 9: 1, 2   Matthew 4: 12-16

A man like John The Baptist would
prepare people for Jesus
Isaiah 40: 3-5   Matthew 3: 1-4

52

JESUS' LATER LIFE

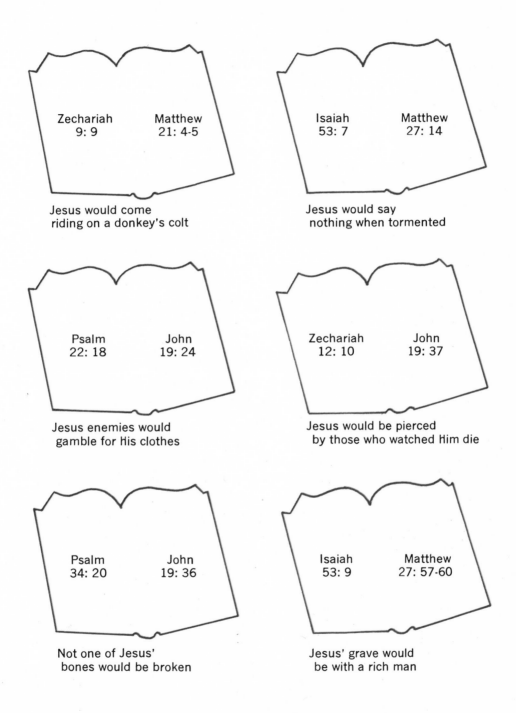

Zechariah 9: 9   Matthew 21: 4-5

Jesus would come
riding on a donkey's colt

Isaiah 53: 7   Matthew 27: 14

Jesus would say
nothing when tormented

Psalm 22: 18   John 19: 24

Jesus enemies would
gamble for His clothes

Zechariah 12: 10   John 19: 37

Jesus would be pierced
by those who watched Him die

Psalm 34: 20   John 19: 36

Not one of Jesus'
bones would be broken

Isaiah 53: 9   Matthew 27: 57-60

Jesus' grave would
be with a rich man

53

Matthew 26: 17-29; Mark 14: 12-25; Luke 22: 7-20, 24-30;
I Corinthians 11: 23-26

The Upstairs Room

Jesus eats the Passover meal with His disciples

The time had come for Jesus to eat His last meal with the twelve disciples. All over Jerusalem people would eat a special meal that night, remembering the time when God helped the Israelites escape from Egypt.

It was a strangely quiet procession that had come into an upstairs room that night. The disciples sensed that something very sad and very important was about to happen. They had walked with Jesus enough to know His feelings.

But even in the midst of this quiet, sacred time, some little jealousies arose. There was the question of who would sit where at this important meal. Of course, everyone wanted the best seats, those closest to Jesus.

Jesus could not help but notice the disciples hurrying to get to the best seats. They didn't even stop to wash their feet. Since people wore sandals on the dusty roads, they always had their feet washed when they came in.

Usually a servant or slave would come to wash the guests' feet. But there were no servants or slaves at this supper. There was only

Jesus—and His twelve chosen followers. Certainly no one of those twelve would put himself below the others to do the work of a servant.

When the scuffling had ended and all the disciples had found the best seats they could get, Jesus took off His outer garment. The disciples were puzzled as He took a pitcher of water and poured some in a basin. Perhaps Jesus was going to wash His own feet. No one had offered to do it for Him. Certainly no one was going to jump up now and lose his seat at the table.

Then Jesus kneeled down before one of His disciples and began to wash his feet. From disciple to disciple He went, silently washing the dust of the road from their feet, and drying them with a towel.

There was a great silence in the room. Only the splashing of the water could be heard and the sounds of Jesus washing His servants' feet. The disciples felt so ashamed of themselves. If only they could come into that room again, they would hurry to wash Jesus' feet. Now He was doing a servant's work for them. But why? They felt terrible about it.

When Jesus came at last to Peter, the fisherman was filled with shame. He couldn't let his Master go through with that.

"Lord, are You going to wash my feet?" he asked. Peter knew that Jesus was God's Son. How could he let the Son of God stoop down and clean his dirty feet?

"You don't know what I'm doing now," Jesus said quietly. "But you will understand later."

"You'll never wash my feet," Peter cried out. He wouldn't let Him. He would hide his feet so Jesus couldn't do it.

"I must," said Jesus. "If I don't, you will not be part of My plans."

Peter certainly would not have that happen. More than anything in the world, he wanted to be with Jesus and please Him.

55

"Then wash my hands and my head also," Peter blurted out.

When Jesus came to Judas, the traitor's heart began to beat faster. He looked down at the dust on his feet. Some of that dust had clung to his feet when he went to tell the Pharisees about Jesus.

Judas' heart and mind were filled with guilt as he watched Jesus wash that dust from his feet, then gently wipe his feet with a towel. When Jesus looked up at him, their eyes met. Somehow Judas knew that Jesus had looked inside at all the evil plans. Quickly he turned his eyes away, for he could not look any more at the face of Jesus.

At last Jesus was finished. He put on His outer garments again and sat down at the table. The twelve were so stunned by Jesus' humble act that they could say nothing. So they waited, hoping Jesus would tell them why He had done this.

"Do you know what I have done to you?" Jesus asked them. "You call Me Teacher and Lord, and that is true. But I, your Teacher and Lord, have stooped to do a servant's work. If I have washed your feet, shouldn't you also be willing to do such things for each other?"

The disciples looked around the table at each other. As their eyes met, all the selfish pride disappeared. Never again would they hurry for the best seats. Never again would they claim to be the greatest. At the first sign of pride or selfishness, they would forever see in their minds God's Son, quietly and humbly washing their feet.

Then Jesus spoke to His disciples again. "One of you here at this table is going to betray Me."

Judas sat up straight and shifted his eyes around the room. Jesus knew what he was going to do! But how could He? Suddenly Judas felt like running away. He wanted to run from the room into the dark night. His sin was uncovered. What would Jesus do now?

The other disciples, though, did not suspect who that traitor

*The disciples were ashamed when Jesus
began to wash their feet.*

was. Judas had been such a good actor that he had deceived them all.

The other disciples felt terrible at the news that there was a traitor among them. They looked at each other with suspicious eyes. Which one of them would do such a thing?

One by one, the disciples began to ask aloud, "Lord, is it I?"

Now John was sitting at Jesus' right side. Peter, sitting next to John, whispered in his ear, "Ask Jesus who it is." Then John leaned close to Jesus and whispered so softly that the other disciples didn't hear, "Lord, who is it?"

While the others talked sadly among themselves, Jesus whispered back to John, "It is the one to whom I give this piece of bread when I dip it."

When Jesus said that, He dipped His bread in the dish before Him and gave it to Judas. Slowly Judas reached out to take the bread. Then his eyes met Jesus' eyes again. Jesus kept looking at Judas as He spoke. "Woe to that man who betrays Me," He said. "It would be better if he had not been born."

The other disciples had looked now to see what Jesus was doing. All other talking stopped as Jesus spoke to Judas. "What you are going to do, do quickly," He said.

Judas could stay no longer at the supper. Jesus had seen what was in his heart and mind and Judas knew it. The traitor had been discovered. Quickly he jumped up from the table and hurried out of the room.

"Where is Judas going?" one of the disciples whispered.

"Jesus must have sent him to buy something," another disciple whispered back. "Or perhaps he's going to give to the poor."

But Judas was not going out to buy or give. As he hurried from the room, he turned for one last glance at the Man he would betray. Jesus' eyes were still fastened upon him.

58

Judas felt Jesus' eyes look into his heart.

Trembling as he felt Jesus' eyes look into his heart, Judas ran out into the dark streets.

After Judas left, Jesus took some of the bread in His hands and began to pray. When He finished, He broke it into pieces and gave some to each of His disciples.

"Take this," He said. "Eat it, for it is My body."

When the bread was eaten, Jesus took the cup of wine and began to pray again. Perhaps He looked across the years as He lifted that cup, seeing all the thousands and thousands of His followers who would drink from the communion cup in their churches. Quietly He thanked God for the cup and all it would mean to His followers.

When Jesus finished praying, He passed the cup to His disciples. "All of you drink from this," He said. "This is My blood which is poured out for many."

It was the custom to end the Passover supper with singing. The hymn that most people of Israel sang had the beautiful words from

"Eat this, for it is My body," Jesus told His disciples.

60

Psalms 13 through 18. Never had those words meant more than they did that night in the upper room as Jesus sang them with His disciples.

> What shall I do for the Lord
> For all His gifts to me?
> I will lift up the cup of salvation
> And call on His name.
> Precious in God's sight
> Is the death of His saints.

Throughout all the years of their lives, the disciples would never forget that night as they sang that beautiful hymn together. Nor would they forget the voice of Jesus singing above all the others as He looked up toward Heaven.

The most important supper of all time had ended. The time had come for Jesus and His disciples to leave the upstairs room and go out into the dark night—the night that would lead toward the cross.

SOMETHING TO THINK ABOUT

1. How would you feel if the greatest man you know took off your shoes and washed your feet? Would you feel embarrassed that such a great person should do such work for you? Think how the disciples must have felt when Jesus washed their feet.
2. Jesus' last supper with His disciples was more than just a meal together. It was a meal to remember for all time. Jesus said we should eat and drink in the same way to remember Him. That is the reason why your church has a communion service.
3. The next time your church has a communion service, think of the night long ago when Jesus ate with His disciples. Think also of the following day when He died on the cross for you. Then thank Him for all He did for you.
4. Why do you think that Jesus died for you? Was it because He loves you? If Jesus loves you enough to die for you, will you love Him enough to live for Him? Will you tell others so they can love Him and live for Him, too?

JESUS' LAST SUPPER

THE FOOD JESUS AND HIS DISCIPLES ATE

MENU

- UNLEAVENED BREAD—THIN, HEAVY CAKES OF BREAD, MADE WITHOUT YEAST OR LEAVEN

- RED WINE, MIXED WITH TWICE ITS AMOUNT OF WATER

- BITTER HERBS

- VINEGAR OR SALT WATER, IN WHICH THE BITTER HERBS WERE DIPPED

- CHAROSETH—A MIXTURE OF ALMONDS, RAISINS, APPLES, AND OTHER FOODS. AFTER THE BITTER HERBS WERE DIPPED IN VINEGAR OR SALT WATER, THEY WERE DIPPED IN THIS THICK MIXTURE WHICH REMINDED PEOPLE OF THE CLAY WHICH THE ISRAELITES USED TO MAKE BRICKS IN EGYPT.

THE SOP OR MORSEL—The wafer or cake of unleavened bread was curled up like a potato chip. It was used instead of silverware to dip food from a dish, just as we would dip a potato chip into a spread. The sop and food were then eaten together.

62

THE FURNITURE JESUS AND HIS DISCIPLES USED

It has been hundreds of years since Jesus and His disciples ate the Last Supper together. Can we know what kind of furniture they had in the upper room?

We can't know exactly, because the Bible does not tell us. But other ancient writings do tell what some customs were like in Bible times. Some of these writings tell us about the furniture used for dining.

In most pictures, you will see Jesus and the disciples sitting in chairs. This was probably not true. At that time, people in Bible lands lay on their left sides to eat, with an arm propped up on pillows, and head upright.

People lay like this on a divan, something like a couch, with head toward the table and feet away from the table. There were twelve of these couches around the table in the upper room.

The table in the upper room was a very long table made of wood. The couches were arranged around three sides of the table, leaving the fourth side empty. The empty end of the table did not have a cloth on it, but the rest of the table did.

The host lay facing the center of the table. The most honored place was at His left. Judas apparently grabbed this couch first. John took the couch at Jesus' right side. Peter sat in the last couch on the other side of the table, the place of least honor. We do not know which disciples sat in the other couches.

But when Jesus washed the disciples' feet, He began with Peter, sitting in the place of least honor. Perhaps Jesus was showing how the "last shall be first" (Matthew 19: 30).

63

Gethsemane

*A time of decision
and betrayal*

Quietly the disciples left the upper room with Jesus and made their way out into the dark streets of the city. They walked through the great eastern gate overlooking the deep Kidron Valley, down through the valley, and up through the shadowy groves of olive trees. At last they came to a garden called Gethsemane.

Jesus and His disciples had come to this garden many times, invited by a friend who owned it. Under the olive trees Jesus had often sat, talking with His disciples about God's work.

On this night, with only the stars and moon to light their path, Jesus and His disciples made their way through the olive trees to their familiar meeting place. The disciples listened carefully as Jesus talked with them.

"Tonight you will all be scattered," Jesus told them. "You will all leave Me."

Peter could not bear to think of such a thing. "Lord," he said. "The others may do that, but I'll never leave You."

Jesus, with pity in His eyes, looked at Peter. "This very night, before the cock crows at daybreak, you will say three times that you never knew Me."

"No, no!" said Peter. "I wouldn't do that even if I had to die for you."

Then the other disciples began to say the same thing. They could never turn against Jesus. Never!

Jesus said nothing more about the matter. The disciples would learn soon enough what they would do.

"Wait here," Jesus told the group. "I must go alone and pray."

Then Jesus took with Him Peter, James, and John. He wanted them closer to His place of prayer. Perhaps they could pray, too, while they waited.

"My soul is very sorrowful, even to death," Jesus whispered to the three as they walked apart from the others. "Stay here and watch with Me." How Jesus longed for someone to share in His suffering there in the garden. Surely these three, more than any other people on earth, would stay there. Surely they would pray, too, when they knew how He felt.

But it was now long past the disciples' bedtime and they were very sleepy. Jesus had not been gone long before they were all fast asleep.

While the disciples slept, Jesus held the most important prayer meeting the world has ever known. Burdened by the thought of bearing the sins of the world. Jesus fell to His knees and poured out His heart to His Father.

"Father, if there is some other way, let this terrible thing pass away from Me," He pleaded. "But do what You know best, not what I want."

When Jesus had prayed for some time, He went back to talk with His three best friends. Perhaps He could share with them some of the glorious things He had heard from His Father. Perhaps they could talk with Him as He began to bear this heavy weight of the world's sin.

Jesus prayed alone while His disciples slept.

But the disciples were fast asleep.

"Couldn't you watch with Me for one hour?" He whispered to Peter. The fisherman looked up sheepishly into his Master's face. How could he have fallen asleep when Jesus needed him? By then James and John were awake, so they sat up straight while Jesus went back to pray again.

When Jesus came back, He found the three fast asleep once more. The soft night air had been too much. Only His Father could comfort Him now.

So Jesus returned to pray a third time. The weight of the world's sin was pressing upon Him so much as He prayed that sweat came from Him "like great drops of blood." Then suddenly a wonderful thing happened. Out of Heaven an angel came to give the comfort no one else would share.

How long the angel stayed or what he said, no one on earth will ever know. But it was enough. At last Jesus arose and went back to His disciples. Looking across the Kidron Valley to the twinkling lights of the city, Jesus could see now the soldiers and Temple guards coming through the gate, lighting their way with torches. The time had come when He would be betrayed into the hands of His enemies.

The time had also come for the disciples to wake from their sleep, for the enemy was near.

"Rise," Jesus called to them. "Let us be going. My betrayer is almost here."

The disciples sat up with a start. What was Jesus saying?

Then the murmur of many voices nearby drove out all the remaining sleep from them. Quickly the disciples jumped up to see a crowd of rude people coming toward them with clubs and swords, lighting the way with torches.

Jesus had talked much about dying soon, but somehow they

hadn't thought it would be now, or in this way. Frightened at the sudden turn of events, the disciples stood by helplessly. Peter grabbed the only sword in their group, ready to fight to the death for his Master.

Then Peter and the others saw Judas. He was right there at the front of the crowd. They were stunned with the thought that one of their own had brought Jesus' enemies to their secret hiding place. So that was why Judas had gone out of the upper room so quickly!

Before anyone could do a thing, Jesus walked straight toward the mob. "Whom do you seek?" Jesus asked.

It was too dark to see who had spoken, so the mob didn't recognize Him. "We want Jesus of Nazareth!" they shouted.

Jesus kept on walking toward them. The mob began to stop and move aside for Him. "I am He!" Jesus said with a stern voice.

All the loud shouting in the mob stopped at once. In fear the people jumped away from Jesus and fell down on the ground.

"Who are you looking for?" Jesus asked again.

A few weak voices came from the mob, still lying on the ground. "Jesus of Nazareth," they said.

"I told you that I am He!" Jesus said.

One by one the people in the mob stood up. When they saw that Jesus was not going to fight them, they picked up their clubs and swords, waiting for Judas to give the signal.

At last Judas rushed forward toward Jesus and kissed Him. "Hail, Master," he said. There was no doubt about it now. This was the Man they were seeking. Judas had identified Him. The signal to capture Him had been given—Judas' kiss of death.

Immediately the mob surged forward and seized Jesus. How long they had waited for this moment to capture Him! The leaders would certainly reward them for His capture.

"Have you come out as though you were capturing a robber?"

"Couldn't you watch with Me for one hour?"
Jesus asked.

Jesus asked them while they bound His hands. "Day after day I was with you in the Temple, but you didn't take Me then."

Suddenly Peter realized that these people were going to take Jesus away. It was time to act! Rushing forward, he started slashing at them with his sword.

"Stop, Peter!" Jesus called to him. "Don't you think I could call

*Peter's sword found its mark
and cut off the ear of Malchus.*

down twelve legions of angels to fight for Me?" Peter had known
this, of course. He knew that Jesus could do anything.

But Jesus had not spoken soon enough. Already Peter's sword
had found its mark and had cut off the ear of a man named Malchus. But even as the man cried out in pain, Jesus touched the
wound. As quickly as the man had lost his ear, he was healed.

"Put up your sword, Peter," Jesus told him. "Those who fight
with the sword will die by the sword."

Turning to the mob again, Jesus showed His love for His disciples. "I am the One you want," He said. "Let My followers go."

But even as the mob turned to look, His followers were gone.
They had all "forsook Him and fled." Now Jesus was alone before
the mob in Gethsemane.

70

SOMETHING TO THINK ABOUT

1. Do you like to sit down and talk with your father when things become difficult? That's what happened when Jesus prayed in the garden of Gethsemane. The crucifixion was near and Jesus was feeling the weight of the world's sin pressing upon Him. What better place could He go than to His Father in Heaven? What could He do but pray?

2. That's a good lesson for us to learn, too. When things get difficult, we should talk with our father and mother. But we should also remember to talk with our Heavenly Father, for He knows all about us and He knows all about the problems which we face. What could you do that would be more important?

3. When Jesus prayed, God sent an angel to comfort Him. Have you ever thought that God might also send an angel to comfort you when you pray? You can't see God and you can't see His angels, but sometimes we sense that God or His angel is near us when we pray to Him. Prayer is not merely talking to God, it's also bringing God near us. Can you think of anything better when we need help than to have God near us?

71

THE GARDEN OF GETHSEMANE

East of the Golden Gate, the large gate in the walls of Jerusalem near the Temple, lies the Kidron Valley. It is a deep valley running along the eastern wall of the city. Farther east, the land rises sharply into the Mount of Olives.

The Garden of Gethsemane is today a small grove of ancient olive trees, on the western slope of the Mount of Olives, looking toward Jerusalem. Here, in this lovely place, Jesus often went to be alone and pray. It may have been a private grove of olive trees, owned by a friend.

While in the Garden of Gethsemane, one may look across the Kidron Valley and see the walls of Jerusalem. It is easy to see the entire Temple area from this place. So, while Jesus was there, He could look across to His Father's house in the city. He could probably see also the hill of Calvary, where He was to die.

The Garden of Gethsemane has been set aside as a churchyard

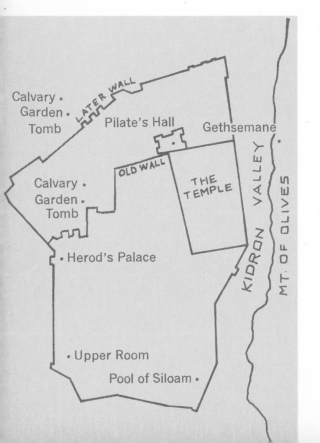

Many of the events of Jesus' life took place near the Garden of Gethsemane. Nearby, He began His triumphal entry into Jerusalem. From the Mount of Olives, He ascended into Heaven. His temptation at the pinnacle of the Temple was just across the valley. His death at Calvary was on the other side of the city.

Looking west from the Garden of Gethsemane, the ancient walls of Jerusalem may still be seen near the Temple area.

in our times. There are some ancient olive trees which must be almost two thousand years old. An ancient historian, Josephus, says the Roman Emperor Titus destroyed all trees around Jerusalem in 70 A.D., so these probably grew up since that time.

The large mass of rock where Jesus prayed is still in the Garden of Gethsemane.   Part of it can be seen behind the church and part of it is inside the church, near the altar.

Only a short distance to the east is the village of Bethany, where Jesus visited Mary and Martha and Lazarus, and where he brought Lazarus back to life.

73

Matthew 26: 58, 69-72; Mark 14: 54, 66-72; Luke 22: 54-62;
John 18: 15-18, 25-27

Before the Cock Crows

Peter denies Jesus

In the cold, dark hours of the night, while Jesus was on trial,
Peter sat by a fire in the courtyard. Soldiers and servants of the
high priest had built the fire to keep warm while they waited for
the trial to end.

When the disciples had run away in Gethsemane, only Peter
and John dared to follow their Master to the trial. Since John knew
some people in the high priest's household, he was allowed to come
inside to watch the trial. Once inside, John persuaded one of the
women to let Peter in, too.

But while John watched the trial, Peter waited out in the courtyard. The fisherman had bravely faced storms on the Sea of Galilee.
But he could not face the religious leaders. He was afraid. He
wondered what would happen next.

While Peter warmed himself by the fire a young woman came
near. She knew that Peter was a disciple, for John had asked her
to let Peter in. The young woman began to talk with Peter.

"You were with Jesus, too, weren't you?" she asked.

Peter looked up from the fire and saw the soldiers and servants
of the high priest staring at him. These were the same people who

74

While Peter warmed himself by the fire, a young woman came near.

had captured Jesus a few minutes before. If they took Jesus, they would probably capture him, too.

"I . . . I don't know what you mean," Peter answered. Peter's heart began to beat faster.

Quickly Peter left the fire and went over by the porch. But he was soon recognized there, too. Another woman who saw him pointed to Peter. "This man was with Jesus of Nazareth," she said.

Again, Peter saw the eyes of Jesus' enemies looking at him. Again his heart was full of fear.

"I don't know the Man," Peter cried out.

Peter didn't know where to go now. He must stay nearby to see what would happen to his Master. While he thought about his next move, a man came up to him. He was a relative of Malchus, the man whom Peter had injured in Gethsemane. Behind him were others from the high priest's household.

Peter knew he was in trouble now. This man would certainly want revenge because Peter had cut off Malchus' ear. What should he do?

"Didn't I see you in the garden with Jesus?" the man asked. "He's one of the followers."

"He must be," said another. "He talks like a Galilean."

Peter felt desperate now. He was sure this group of men would pounce upon him and kill him.

In his moment of fear, Peter began to curse. "I don't even know the Man," he kept saying to them.

But even as he spoke, Peter heard footsteps behind him. Looking up, his eyes met the eyes of Jesus, being led from one building to another.

In the distance, the sound of a rooster's crow mingled with the faint light of early dawn. Suddenly Peter remembered what Jesus had said the night before, "Before the cock crows, you will deny Me three times."

A terrible feeling of guilt swept over the fisherman. What had he done? With all his talk of loyalty, he had turned against his Master, and Jesus had heard him.

Heartbroken, Peter ran from the courtyard. As he ran blindly down the streets, he cried like a little child.

76

Jesus had heard what Peter said and turned to look at His disciple.

SOMETHING TO THINK ABOUT

1. How do you think Peter felt when he cursed and said he did not know Jesus? How would you have felt if you had been Peter that morning?
2. Have you ever been tempted to say to your friends, "I don't believe in Jesus," or "I don't like to go to church," or something like that?

WHAT THE GOSPELS SAY
ABOUT SIMON PETER

- HIS HOMETOWN WAS BETHSAIDA
  JOHN 1: 44

- HIS FATHER'S NAME WAS
  JOHN OR JONAH
  MATTHEW 16: 17, JOHN 1: 42

- HE AND ANDREW WERE FISHING
  PARTNERS WITH ZEBEDEE'S SONS,
  JAMES AND JOHN LUKE 5: 10

- HE WAS MARRIED
  MARK 1: 30

- HE MET JESUS WHEN HE CAME TO
  HEAR JOHN THE BAPTIST PREACH
  JOHN 1: 35-40

- HIS BROTHER ANDREW
  BROUGHT HIM TO JESUS
  JOHN 1: 40, 41

- JESUS CHANGED HIS NAME
  FROM SIMON TO PETER
  JOHN 1: 42

PETER
THE
FISHERMAN

- HE MOVED TO CAPERNAUM WITH
  JESUS EARLY IN JESUS' MINISTRY
  MARK 1: 21, 29

- HE WAS CALLED TO BE JESUS'
  FULL-TIME DISCIPLE
  MATTHEW 4: 18-22

- HIS MOTHER-IN-LAW WAS
  HEALED BY JESUS
  LUKE 4: 38-41

- HE WAS CHOSEN TO BE ONE OF
  JESUS' TWELVE APOSTLES
  LUKE 6: 12-16

- WITH THE OTHER APOSTLES,
  HE RECEIVED POWER TO
  HEAL AND DRIVE OUT DEMONS
  MATTHEW 9: 35—11: 1

- HE WALKED ON THE SEA OF GALILEE
  MATTHEW 14: 28-31

- AT CAESAREA PHILIPPI, HE TOLD
  JESUS THAT HE WAS GOD'S SON
  MATTHEW 16: 16

- HE WENT WITH JESUS WHEN
  HE WAS TRANSFIGURED
  MATTHEW 17: 1-8

- HE CAUGHT A FISH WITH
  A COIN FOR TAXES
  MATTHEW 17: 24-27

- HE ASKED JESUS HOW MANY TIMES
  A PERSON SHOULD FORGIVE
  MATTHEW 18: 21, 22

- JESUS WARNED HIM THAT
  HE WOULD DENY HIS LORD
  JOHN 13: 38

- HE WENT APART WITH JESUS WHEN
  HE PRAYED IN GETHSEMANE
  MATTHEW 26: 27

- HE CUT OFF MALCHUS' EAR
  JOHN 18: 10

PETER
THE
PREACHER

- HE FOLLOWED JESUS TO THE
  HIGH PRIEST'S HOME
  JOHN 18: 15, 16

- HE DENIED JESUS,
  THEN HE WEPT ABOUT IT
  MARK 14: 66-72

- MARY MAGDALENE FOUND HIM AND
  TOLD HIM THAT
  JESUS' TOMB WAS EMPTY
  JOHN 20: 2, 3

- HE WENT WITH JOHN
  TO SEE JESUS' TOMB
  JOHN 20: 2-7

- JESUS SHOWED HIMSELF TO PETER
  LUKE 24: 34

PETER AND OTHERS FISHED AT
GALILEE. JESUS HELPED THEM
CATCH MANY FISH
JOHN 21

79

The King
Who Said Nothing

Jesus before Pilate and Herod

It was still early in the morning when Jesus' captors dragged Him before the Roman governor, Pilate. Pilate was not happy that he had to sit in judgment so early. What was the hurry? Why were the leaders rushing to get this Man condemned?

But to please the leaders, Pilate sat down in his chair and called for the Prisoner to be brought in. Surely He must be a criminal if they wanted Him killed so quickly.

When Jesus was brought into the room, Pilate was shocked to see that He was not a vicious criminal, but a quiet, peaceful Man with kind eyes. Surely this could not be the right person.

The religious leaders had stayed outside Pilate's hall, for to come inside this Roman building on the Passover would make them unclean. They felt they could murder a Man and still be clean, but to go into Pilate's hall would make them unclean. It was the type of thing for which Jesus had scolded them.

Pilate hurried out to talk with the leaders. There had to be some mistake. This Man they had brought was no criminal!

"With what are you accusing Him?" Pilate asked the leaders.

The leaders did not like for Pilate to question them. If they felt Jesus should die, that should be enough.

"If He weren't a criminal, we wouldn't have brought Him to you," they shouted back to Pilate.

Pilate was angry. He didn't like the way these people were talking.

"Then take Him back and judge Him by your own laws," he answered.

But the religious leaders didn't want that. They could not put a man to death. Only the Romans could do that, for they were in charge of the country at that time.

Then all of the leaders began to shout at once. Each had something bad to say about Jesus.

"He's trying to start trouble in the country," said some.

"He won't let us give money to Caesar," said others.

"He claims to be a king," some said.

Pilate hurried back to Jesus. With all that the leaders had said against Him, surely Jesus would shout back angrily to say how innocent He was. But Pilate was surprised. Jesus stood quietly. He did not say a word.

"Don't you hear what those people are saying about You?" Pilate asked. "Don't you have anything to say to answer them?"

But Jesus stood quietly listening to the cries of the people outside. Why should He, a King, try to answer the lies of such people?

Never before had such a prisoner been before Pilate. "What kind of a Person is this?" Pilate wondered. Perhaps this Man was of royal blood. He certainly looked like He could be a king. Perhaps half to himself and half aloud, Pilate asked Jesus about it.

"Are you really the King of the Jews?" he asked.

Jesus looked into Pilate's eyes. Did Pilate want to know the truth?

"Are you asking this for yourself or because someone else said it about Me?" Jesus asked.

"I'm not a Jew," Pilate answered. "Your own people have sent you here. What have you done to get them so upset?"

Then Jesus told Pilate about His kingdom. "It is not in this world," He said. "If it were, my servants would fight for Me."

It was true. If Jesus had stirred up the country as much as the leaders said, there must be hundreds or thousands who would fight for Him. But there was no fighting, no revolution going on.

"But You are a king, then?" Pilate asked.

"You say that I am," said Jesus. "I came into the world to tell people about the truth. People who want the truth listen to Me."

Pilate thought for a moment. "But what is truth?" he asked.

Pilate would have stayed to talk more with Jesus, but the crowd

82

The leaders were angry that Pilate would question them.

of people outside was getting louder. If anyone started a revolution, it would be those people.

Then Pilate went back to pronounce judgment. All the people became very quiet to hear what he would say.

"I can't find anything wrong with this Man," Pilate said.

When Pilate said that, the religious leaders and their friends began to shout in anger. "He stirs up the people, all the way to Galilee," they cried out.

Now when Pilate heard "Galilee," he thought of a way to get out of this.

"Is this Man from Galilee?" Pilate asked. "Then I'll send Him to Herod. He's here in Jerusalem right now."

Herod was glad to see Jesus. He had heard so many things about Him, but had never met Him. He had heard of all the wonderful things Jesus had done, so perhaps Jesus would do some magic tricks for him.

It was a strange meeting that day between Herod and Jesus. The religious leaders stood by, screaming terrible things about Jesus while Herod kept asking Him questions. But through all of this, Jesus kept silent. At last, Herod grew tired of asking questions. It was no longer fun since he couldn't get answers.

So Herod called for a royal robe and put it on Jesus. Then he and his guards laughed and made fun of the new King.

But when Herod grew tired of this, he sent Jesus back to Pilate. He couldn't find a thing wrong with Him. Now it was up to Pilate again. Pilate must decide if Jesus was to live or die.

SOMETHING TO THINK ABOUT

1. The leaders who brought Jesus to Pilate wanted to kill Him. They hated Jesus because He did not obey their strict rules and because He said He was God's Son. So, even though they had seen Jesus do many wonderful miracles, they would not believe that He was more than a man.
2. Have you ever known other people who would not believe in Jesus? They have read about His miracles and know that He is God's Son, but they refuse to believe. Are they different from the Pharisees and their friends?
3. The Bible teaches clearly that Jesus is the Son of God. It tells of many things which He did, even bringing dead people back to life. Only the Son of God could do that!
4. Before Pilate sent Jesus to Herod, he said that he could find nothing wrong with Jesus. Why didn't he set Jesus free then? Do you think the Pharisees would have started a riot if Pilate had done that? Then Pilate might have lost his job. Like the Pharisees, Pilate was putting his job ahead of Jesus, even though he knew that Jesus was innocent of anything wrong.
5. Many people today put their jobs ahead of Jesus, too. Some put their friends ahead of Him, or their pleasure, or their love of money. There are so many things that we can put ahead of Jesus in our lives. Look into your own life. See if you are putting other things ahead of Jesus. If you are, ask yourself which should be first in your life.

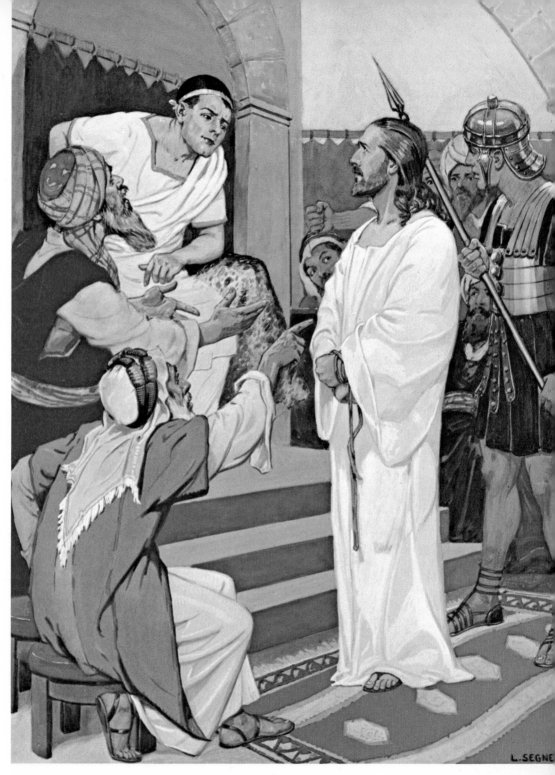

Herod wanted Jesus to perform a miracle or some magic tricks for him.

85

HEROD'S FAMILY

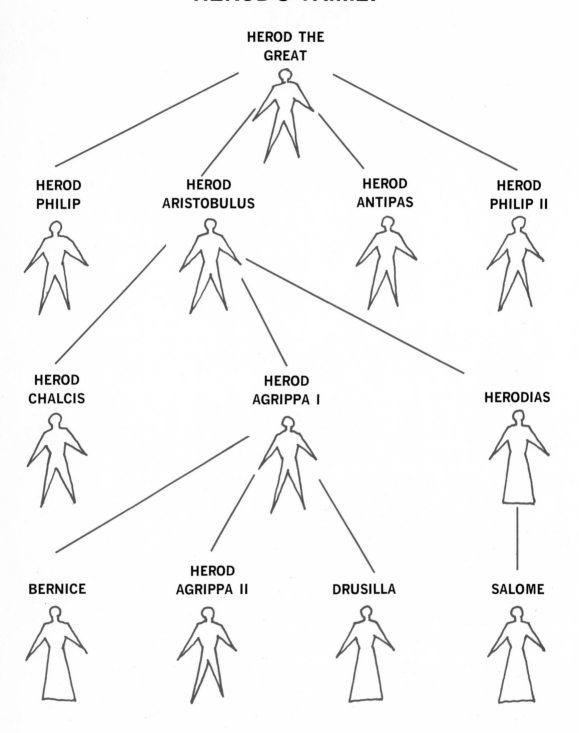

HEROD THE
GREAT

HEROD
PHILIP

HEROD
ARISTOBULUS

HEROD
ANTIPAS

HEROD
PHILIP II

HEROD
CHALCIS

HEROD
AGRIPPA I

HERODIAS

BERNICE

HEROD
AGRIPPA II

DRUSILLA

SALOME

HEROD THE GREAT	Tried to kill the baby Jesus when he killed all the babies around Bethlehem. Matthew 2: 1-18
HEROD PHILIP	First husband of his niece, Herodias. Father of Salome. Mark 6: 17-19
HEROD ARISTOBULUS	Father of Herodias, Chalcis, and Agrippa I. Grandfather of Salome.
HEROD ANTIPAS	(Herod the tetrarch) Second husband of Herodias. Killed John the Baptist (Mark 6: 14-29) and judged Jesus before He was crucified. Luke 23: 7-12
HEROD PHILIP II	Husband of his great-niece, Salome.
HEROD CHALCIS	Husband of his niece, Bernice.
HEROD AGRIPPA I	Killed James, the apostle, (Acts 12: 1-2) and put Peter into prison (Acts 12: 3-11). Father of Bernice, Drusilla, and Agrippa II.
HERODIAS	Mother of Salome. Wife of Herod Philip, then Antipas. Planned the death of John the Baptist. Mark 6: 14-29
BERNICE	Wife of her uncle, Herod Chalcis. Was with Agrippa II when he tried Paul. Acts 25: 13
HEROD AGRIPPA II	"King Agrippa" before whom Paul was tried. Acts 25: 13—26: 32
DRUSILLA	Wife of Felix, the governor who tried Paul. Acts 23: 26—24: 27
SALOME	Wife of great uncle, Herod Philip II. Danced before her step-father, Antipas, for John the Baptist's head. Mark 6: 14-29)

Matthew 27: 15-26; Mark 15: 6-15;
Luke 23: 13-25; John 18: 39—19: 16

*A messenger brought word
to Pilate from his wife.*

Hands That Could Never Get Clean

Pilate passes judgment on Jesus

When Herod could find nothing wrong with Jesus, he sent Him back to Pilate. Why should he sentence Him to death? Let Pilate do what he wanted.

But Pilate's wife had a nightmare. She dreamed about some things that would happen if Jesus was harmed. Quickly she sent word to Pilate, who had been too busy that morning to see her.

"Don't do anything to that good Man," the message said. "I've had a terrible dream today about Him."

Pilate was frightened when he heard this. Surely this was no ordinary Man before him.

88

So Pilate brought Jesus out before the people. "You brought this Man to me as a criminal," he said. "But I cannot find a thing wrong with Him. Neither can Herod. I'm going to beat Him and then let Him go."

"Look at this Man!" Herod said to the people. But even though Jesus was suffering, the people were not satisfied.

When Pilate said that, the priests and their followers began to cry out with a loud voice, "No, no!" they cried. "You must not let Him go!"

Then Pilate had an idea. Often the Romans let a man go free during the Passover. He would give them such a poor choice that they could not help but let Jesus go.

90

"I will release a man to you," said Pilate. "You may choose between Jesus or Barabbas. Which will it be?"

Now Barabbas was a murderer. Pilate was sure they would not choose a murderer over this good Man.

But the priests and their followers began to cry out with a loud voice. "Release Barabbas. Release Barabbas," they shouted at Pilate.

"Then what should we do with Jesus?" Pilate asked.

The people began to cry out louder now. The leaders were working them up, turning them into a mob.

"Crucify Him! Crucify Him!" they shouted.

Pilate could scarcely believe it. How could these people do that to an innocent Man?

"Why?" he asked. "What has He done wrong?"

But the people kept shouting and calling for Jesus to be crucified. The religious leaders would never let this Man go now. They hated Him too much.

Pilate would try one more thing. Perhaps this would quiet the mob.

While the people kept shouting, Pilate had Jesus taken to another room. There the soldiers beat Him and pushed a crown made of thorns over His forehead. Then they put on a robe and brought Him back.

"Look at this Man!" Pilate said to the people. How could they help but sympathize with Him now? How could they want anything more to happen to Him? Surely this would be enough punishment for whatever He had done.

But the priests and their followers were not satisfied. They would never be satisfied until Jesus was dead.

"Crucify Him! Crucify Him!" they chanted.

"Crucify Him yourselves!" Pilate shouted at them.

"The law won't let us," they answered. "But He must die because He claims He is God's Son."

When Pilate heard that, he was more frightened than ever. What if this Man were God's Son? What if he should help to crucify God's Son?

Pilate hurried back to talk with Jesus again. "Where did You come from?" he asked. Pilate wanted to know if He had come from God.

But Jesus refused to answer. Surely Pilate knew by now if He was innocent or not.

"Don't You know I have the power to crucify You or let You go?" Pilate said to Jesus. "Why don't You answer me?"

"You have no power at all, except that God has given it to you," Jesus answered. "But those who brought Me here have a greater sin than you."

Once more, Pilate returned to argue with the leaders. He wanted very much to release Jesus. He knew it would be wrong to have Jesus killed.

"If you let this Man go, you are not Caesar's friend," the leaders shouted to Pilate. "We have no king but Caesar."

The leaders stirred up the people so much that Pilate was afraid a riot would break out. At last he ordered a basin of water.

Pilate called for the crowd to be quiet. Then he began to wash his hands before the people. "I am innocent of this Man's blood," said Pilate. "You must take the guilt for His death."

"We will, we will!" the people shouted. "His blood will be on us and our children, not on you."

So Pilate gave orders that Jesus should be crucified. The murderer and robber Barabbas would be set free.

But while they led Jesus away to be crucified, Pilate must have looked at his hands again. Somehow there seemed to be a stain on them. He would never be able to wash it off. It would stay there forever.

SOMETHING TO THINK ABOUT

1. Pilate knew what was right, but he gave in to the crowd. He was afraid of losing his job if he didn't. Do you think Pilate was happy after that.
2. Remember Pilate when you are tempted to give in to the crowd. You can never be happy if you put the crowd ahead of Jesus.

"You are guilty for this Man's death,"
Pilate said to the people as he washed his hands.

PILATE'S JUDGMENT HALL

What was the building where Pilate judged Jesus? Where was it? What was it called? These are questions people often ask about Pilate's judgment hall.

The building where Pilate judged Jesus is sometimes called the Praetorium. Before Pilate's time, the name Praetorium was given to an army headquarters. But in Pilate's time, the name became associated with the home of any Roman governor. Pilate's home in Jerusalem was the Praetorium in that part of the world.

Through the years, most people have believed that the Praetorium was located at the Tower of Antonia. This was the Roman fortress, or castle, which was built on the northwest side of the Temple area. See the picture on page 45 of volume 6. The tower in the upper right hand corner was the Tower of Antonia. It was connected to the Temple. Roman soldiers were stationed there to keep peace. Herod the Great had the tower built and named for his friend, Mark Anthony.

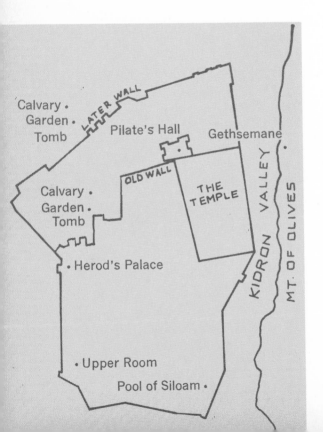

The place where Jesus was judged was joined to His Father's House, the Temple. It seems strange to think that the Temple, built to honor God, should become the home of the Pharisees, who wanted to kill Jesus, and the Roman soldiers who carried out the evil wishes of the Pharisees.

The Tower of Antonia was destroyed, along with the rest of Jerusalem in 70 A.D. Other buildings, such as these, have been built there.

When Paul was captured by the Roman soldiers and taken into the fortress, he was taken into the Tower of Antonia, the same place where Jesus was judged by Pilate. Paul must have thought it a special honor to be tried in the same hall where his Lord had been tried. But while Jesus was beaten inside that hall, Paul was spared a beating because he was a Roman citizen.

Only a few feet away, to the south, was The Holy Place and the Holy of Holies, the place where God dwelled behind the veil. It was this veil which split from top to bottom when Jesus was crucified, showing the people that God could be approached by all men, not only by the high priest. At the Holy Place, the Angel Gabriel had announced the birth of John the Baptist a few years earlier.

Jesus had to carry His own cross until He was too weak.

Matthew 27: 35-44, 55, 56; Mark 15: 24-32, 40, 41; Luke 23: 33-43
John 19: 18-27

The King Upon a Cross

Jesus is crucified

"Please give Him some of this," the women begged.

The soldiers looked down at the jar of wine the women held in their hands. They knew what it was. It was a special mixture of wine with some drug in it. These wealthy women of Jerusalem came to every crucifixion with their drugged wine. When the prisoner drank it, he did not feel the pain so much. It was like someone today getting a shot to keep from hurting when the doctor cuts out his tonsils.

"Oh, all right," the soldiers said. So they dipped a sponge into the drugged wine and held it up to Jesus. But when Jesus knew what it was, He would not drink it. He did not want to face death with a drugged mind.

"Take off His clothes and nail Him to the cross," the centurion shouted. He was the officer in charge of the soldiers.

The soldiers hurried to obey. They took off Jesus' clothes. Then they nailed Him to the cross which was lying on the ground.

"This Man is certainly different," one of the soldiers whispered to another.

"Yes," said the other. "All the others scream and curse us when we nail them to a cross. This Man didn't even take the drugged wine!"

"Listen," said the first soldier. "He's talking. What is He saying?"

The soldiers listened. Then they heard Jesus.

"Father, forgive them," Jesus prayed. "They do not know what they are doing."

The soldiers looked at each other. Never before had anyone prayed for them as they killed him. They felt ashamed.

"We'd better get that sign on the cross," one of the soldiers said. "The centurion gave orders to get it on."

"Jesus of Nazareth, the King of the Jews," the other soldier read as he picked up the sign. "He certainly dies like a king."

Before long, the nailing was finished. The soldiers lifted the heavy cross and dropped the bottom end into a hole which had been dug for it. Then they sat down beneath the cross to gamble for Jesus' clothing.

Around the cross, others came to watch Jesus die. The religious leaders were there. So were the disciples.

"He saved others," the religious leaders mocked, "but He can't save Himself. If He is the King of Israel, let Him come down from the cross. Then we will believe in Him."

Jesus said nothing to these men. He knew they would not believe in Him, even if He came down from the cross. Hadn't He done greater miracles before their eyes? He had even brought dead people back to life.

The soldiers decided to ask the same thing. "If You are the King of the Jews," they said, "why don't You save Yourself?"

Even one of the robbers, hanging on a cross beside Jesus, began to call to Him. "If You are the Messiah, save Yourself and us," he said.

But the other robber did not like to hear such things. He had

*While Jesus died on the cross,
the soldiers gambled for His clothing.*

watched Jesus and wondered. This Man was not like any other man
he had ever seen. Surely He was God's Son.

"Jesus," he begged. "Remember me when You come into Your
kingdom."

Jesus looked at the robber. Here was a criminal who believed in
Him while the religious leaders mocked Him.

"I say to you," Jesus told the robber, "today you will be with Me in Paradise."

Jesus looked down at the people. There was His mother, His aunt Mary, Mary Magdalene, and Salome, John's mother.

"Woman," Jesus said to His mother, "behold your son." Then Jesus spoke to John. "Son," He said, "behold your mother." Mary looked at John. Jesus was asking her to live with John. He was asking John to take care of her. She knew that John would take good care of her.

100

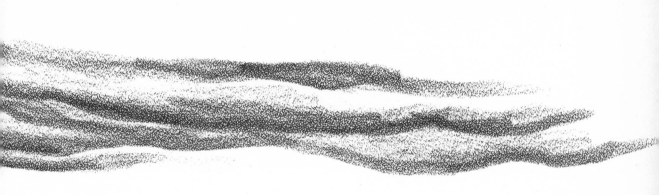

Around the cross,
the people gathered to watch Him die.

By noon, the sky above the three crosses was very dark. It was a quiet, mysterious darkness—like some giant shade drawn between earth and Heaven. The air was still and heavy, as though night were coming.

Many people hurried back through the gates into Jerusalem. They were afraid to stay out in this strange darkness.

At three o'clock that afternoon, the priests in the Temple began to kill the lambs for the evening sacrifice. Many of the priests and leaders had gone back to take care of this chore. If only they had known that the Lamb of God was being killed at that very moment, a sacrifice for the sin of the whole world!

Suddenly the people beneath the cross stood up and looked at Jesus. He was saying something.

"Eli, Eli, lama sabachthani," Jesus cried out. "My God, My God, why have You left Me alone?" Even His Heavenly Father had to turn His back on Jesus as He died for the sins of the world.

Then Jesus cried out again. "It is finished," He said. "Father, into Your hands I give My spirit." Then Jesus died.

At that moment, the earth began to shake and groan. Rocks burst in two. Dead people rose up from the nearby cemetery and walked into Jerusalem to talk with people who had known them.

When these frightening things happened, the soldiers fell to the ground. Surely God was causing these things to happen. What would He do to them? Then the centurion looked up at the center cross.

"This Man really was the Son of God," he whispered.

The priests and their helpers were killing the lambs for the sacrifice when they heard all these terrifying sounds. They stopped for a moment, wondering what was happening. But even as they wondered, the earth trembled again and a loud tearing sound came from within the Temple. The priests hurried to see what had happened.

"Look!" they shouted. "The curtain that hides the Holy of Holies has torn from top to bottom."

This hidden secret place was no longer needed. No longer did the High Priest need to go there to make an offering for sin. The Great High Priest, Jesus Christ, had made that offering now, once and for all.

So the darkest day on earth became the brightest day of all. Jesus had made a new way to Heaven, through Himself.

SOMETHING TO THINK ABOUT

1. What if Jesus had not died on the cross? What would be different today? Would you have a church to go to? Would there be a New Testament to read, or ministers to preach, or Sunday school teachers to teach?
2. If Jesus had not died, how would you get to Heaven? The Bible tells us that His death paid for our sins and gave us a new hope. Jesus is the only way to Heaven. Read John 14: 6. His death gave us eternal life. Will you receive it?

The hill above, called Gordon's Calvary, is thought by many to be the hill on which Jesus was crucified.

JESUS' LAST DAY

**The diagram below shows how Jesus spent the Last Day
before He was crucified.**

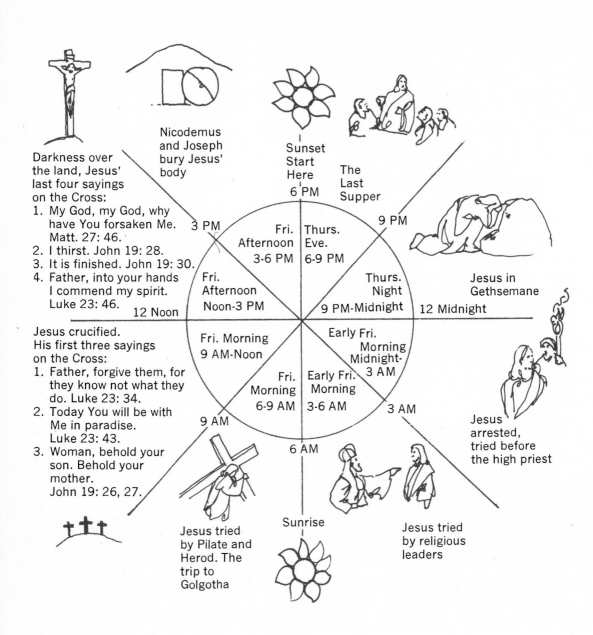

Nicodemus
and Joseph
bury Jesus'
body

Sunset
Start
Here

The
Last
Supper

Darkness over
the land, Jesus'
last four sayings
on the Cross:
1. My God, my God, why
   have You forsaken Me.
   Matt. 27: 46.
2. I thirst. John 19: 28.
3. It is finished. John 19: 30.
4. Father, into your hands
   I commend my spirit.
   Luke 23: 46.

Jesus crucified.
His first three sayings
on the Cross:
1. Father, forgive them, for
   they know not what they
   do. Luke 23: 34.
2. Today You will be with
   Me in paradise.
   Luke 23: 43.
3. Woman, behold your
   son. Behold your
   mother.
   John 19: 26, 27.

6 PM
3 PM
12 Noon
9 AM
6 AM
3 AM
12 Midnight
9 PM

Fri.
Afternoon
3-6 PM

Thurs.
Eve.
6-9 PM

Fri.
Afternoon
Noon-3 PM

Thurs.
Night
9 PM-Midnight

Fri. Morning
9 AM-Noon

Early Fri.
Morning
Midnight-
3 AM

Fri.
Morning
6-9 AM

Early Fri.
Morning
3-6 AM

Jesus in
Gethsemane

Jesus
arrested,
tried before
the high priest

Jesus tried
by Pilate and
Herod. The
trip to
Golgotha

Sunrise

Jesus tried
by religious
leaders

STEP BY STEP WITH JESUS

Thursday Evening, 6 to 9 p.m.

Jesus eats the Last Supper with His disciples in the Upper Room.
Judas leaves the room to meet the religious leaders so he can
take them to Gethsemane.

Thursday Night, 9 p.m. to Midnight

Jesus and His disciples go to the Garden of Gethsemane.
There Jesus prays while the disciples fall asleep.

Early Friday Morning, Midnight to 3 a.m.

Judas leads a band of soldiers and others to Gethsemane.
Jesus is captured and led back into Jerusalem where He is tried
before the high priest.

Early Friday Morning, 3 to 6 a.m.

Jesus is tried before the Sandedrin, the council of religious leaders.
Peter denies that he knows Jesus in the courtyard.

Friday Morning, 6 to 9 a.m.

Pilate talks with Jesus, then sends him to Herod. But Herod sent him
back to Pilate. The crowd forces Pilate to condemn Jesus to death.
Jesus carries His cross and is taken to Golgotha.

Friday Morning, 9 a.m. to Noon.

Jesus is crucified. Roman soldiers nail Him to the cross
and gamble for His clothing.

Friday Afternoon, Noon to 3 p.m.

Darkness covers the earth as Jesus dies. Jesus' death comes
at the time of the sacrifice at the Temple.

Friday Afternoon, 3 to 6 p.m.

Nicodemus and Joseph of Arimathea put spices on Jesus' body
and bury it in a nearby tomb, hurrying to finish before the
Sabbath begins at sundown.

The Empty Tomb

Jesus lives

When the first light of early morning came to the sky east of Jerusalem, Mary Magdalene, Jesus' mother, and the other women from Galilee were up, getting their spices ready to take to Jesus' tomb. They did not know that Nicodemus had already put a hundred pounds of spices on Jesus' body. Nor did they know that the leaders had sealed Jesus' tomb and put a guard around it.

The streets of the city were still dark as the women left their booths made of branches and started toward Golgotha. They hoped to get there by the time it was light enough to see. Then they could do their sad work of putting spices on Jesus' body without curious people watching.

But one question bothered them. "Who will roll the stone away from the tomb?" one of them asked. No one could answer that question, for the stone was very heavy.

At last the women came to the tomb where they had seen Jesus' body laid. It was starting to get light now as they made their way along the path of the garden near the tomb.

But suddenly the women stopped. One of them pointed ahead and cried out. "Look!" she said. "The stone is already rolled away. What has happened?"

*The women were afraid when they saw the two figures
in white by Jesus' tomb.*

The women ran toward the tomb. Then they stopped as they looked ahead of them. Cries of fear rose in their throats. Directly in front of them, sitting on a rock, was a creature whose face shone like lightning and whose clothes were white like snow.

"It's an angel!" the women whispered.

Terrified, the women turned to run away. But behind them the angel's voice rang out.

"Don't be afraid," said the angel. "I know that you are looking

for Jesus. He is not here. He is risen from the dead, as He said He would. Come, let me show you where He lay."

The women could not resist such a wonderful invitation. Quietly they returned and entered the tomb where Jesus' body had been so carefully placed on Friday afternoon.

But there was no body now in the tomb. Instead, another angel, as dazzling as the first, sat at the right side.

"Don't be amazed at what you see," the second angel told the women. "Go and tell Jesus' disciples and Peter that He is going to Galilee and will get there ahead of you. You will see Him there, as He told you."

Trembling and excited, the women hurried from the garden to find the other disciples. They must hear this wonderful news.

When the women found the eleven disciples in the upper room where they had eaten the Last Supper with Jesus, they told the wonderful things they had seen and heard at the tomb.

"We were there at daybreak," one of the women said breathlessly. "We saw two angels."

Then another woman went on with the story. "They told us that Jesus is alive," she said. "He has risen from the dead."

The eleven disciples looked at one another. They knew these women had gone through a terrible time since Jesus had died. Per-

"We saw two angels at the tomb,"
the women told the other disciples.

haps their minds were playing tricks. The strain of Jesus' death had been too much for them. Now they were imagining things.

"But we saw the empty tomb!" the women kept on saying. "We were there."

"Yes," said another. "And one angel told us to tell Peter that Jesus would meet the disciples in Galilee."

"What if this is true?" Peter said at last. "Then we should not be sitting here waiting."

"It's true," John added. "Let's go now and see for ourselves."

The other disciples still did not believe. It simply could not be true. They would not even go to the tomb to see.

But Peter and John were now anxious to find out. Leaving the room, with Mary Magdalene close behind, they began to run toward the garden.

Mary could not hope to keep up with those two. But she went as fast as she could.

Peter and John ran all the way. But John, who was younger, won the race to the tomb. Stooping down, he looked inside. There were the linen cloths, lying inside. But Jesus was gone.

When Peter finally ran up, huffing and puffing, he went right into the tomb. It wasn't like Peter to wait outside.

Peter looked around in amazement. The cloth that had been wrapped around Jesus' head was still lying there, just as it had been put on Jesus. No one had touched it!

The two disciples were very puzzled. Why would a thief stop to roll the cloth so neatly? Who would take Jesus away? Why?

Slowly now they made their way back to the city. Passing Mary Magdalene, on her way to the tomb, they told what they had seen. But they could not be sure that Jesus had risen. They had seen no angels. They had seen nothing but an empty tomb and the linen cloths. Surely that was not enough to make them believe that Jesus

110

was alive. They must wait and see. Until they knew more, they would not believe that He was alive.

Mary slowly made her way back to the tomb. Why had she allowed her hopes to rise so high? Peter and John were probably right. Someone had stolen Jesus' body.

Leaning against the outside of the tomb, Mary began to cry. Not only was her Master dead, but His body was stolen.

Suddenly Mary heard voices coming from the empty tomb. What could it be? Stooping down she looked inside. There were the two angels again, sitting at the place where Jesus had been. Mary was so puzzled now. She had not imagined seeing the angels. They were real. She was looking at them now.

"Why are you crying?" the angels asked.

The linen cloths were in the tomb, but Peter and John could see that Jesus was gone.

Mary confessed her doubts at once. There was no use trying to hide her sorrow from them. Perhaps they could help her.

"Because someone has taken Jesus away, and I don't know where they have put Him," she answered.

Before Mary could say anything further to the angels, she heard footsteps on the garden path. Turning around, she saw a Man standing on the path. It must be the gardener who had come to take care of the garden. Perhaps he would know something about Jesus' body.

"Why are you crying?" the Man asked. "Who are you looking for?"

Mary was startled when she heard the man's voice. It sounded so much like another voice that she loved to hear.

"Please sir," she said. "If you have taken Him away, tell me where you have put Him."

Then the Man spoke again. "Mary," He said.

He did not need to say more. She knew now beyond a shadow of a doubt who that Man was. The glory of the resurrection morning swept upon her for she stood face to face with her Lord and Master. It was the voice of Jesus!

Overcome with joy, Mary threw herself before Him, clinging to Him. She would never let Him go again. Nor would the other disciples. They would go anywhere with Him, even to the death, but they would never let Him be taken from them.

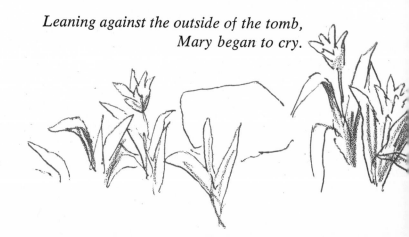

Leaning against the outside of the tomb,
Mary began to cry.

"Don't hold onto Me like that," Jesus told her gently. "I still must go up to be with My Father in Heaven."

Jesus was telling Mary that she could not hold Him. He must return to His heavenly home. He would soon be leaving.

"Go to My brothers and tell them that I am rising to My Father and your Father, to My God and your God," He told Mary.

Mary wanted to stay there with Jesus forever. But she had seen the Lord and she must not keep that wonderful news from her friends. With her heart overflowing with joy, Mary ran from the garden to find the disciples. The angels had been right. Jesus had risen from the dead! She would have no more tears for Jesus—only a heart filled with joy.

SOMETHING TO THINK ABOUT

1. It was difficult for the disciples to believe that Jesus had risen from the dead. They had seen Jesus raise the widow's son at Nain and Lazarus at Bethany. They knew that Jesus had power over death. But it was still hard to believe.
2. Many people today find it hard to believe that Jesus came back to life again after being dead. Yet, the Bible tells us clearly that this happened. More than five hundred people saw Jesus alive after His death.
3. Why is it important to believe in Jesus' resurrection? Could Jesus raise us from the dead if He could not raise Himself to life again? Would we believe that Jesus is "the resurrection and the life" if He had not risen?
4. The resurrection is one of the most important truths in the Bible. It was important for Jesus to die, for through His death He paid the penalty for our sin. But it was important for Him to live again, for by His resurrection, He broke the power of death over us all. See II Corinthians 4: 14, Philippians 3: 10, and Colossians 3: 1.
5. If God can give life to His people once, can He not give it to them a second time? Many refuse to believe that God can raise people from the dead, even though God made these people and gave them life.

114

*The glory of the resurrection morning swept over Mary
as she saw her Lord and Master.*

North of the Damascus Gate of Old Jerusalem is this tomb, where Jesus may have been buried. It is near Gordon's Calvary (see page 103).

THE GARDEN TOMB

Where did Jesus die? Where was He buried? There are two locations where these important events could have taken place.

Many people believe that Jesus died on the hill just north of the Damascus Gate of Old Jerusalem. This hill is called Gordon's Calvary, named after the man who first pointed it out as a possible

116

place for Calvary. Only a few feet from this hill, an ancient tomb has been found, matching the description of the tomb in which Jesus was buried. Around this tomb, a beautiful garden has been built.

But other people think that Jesus was crucified west of the old city walls. Over that place a church has been built, called the Church of the Holy Sepulchre. The Via Dolorosa, or the Way of the Cross, is a route through the old city streets, leading from Pilate's judgment hall to the place where this church has been built. The tomb would have been near this place.

Too many years have gone by, and too many changes have been made in Jerusalem to make anyone sure of the location of these two events. It must be remembered that Jerusalem was completely destroyed in 70 A.D. by the Romans. Since that time, even some of the hills have been excavated and changed.

But we do know that Jesus was crucified and buried just outside the gates of the city walls of that day. These two locations are not more than a few hundred feet apart. It was somewhere near one of these two places where Jesus died and was buried in a tomb, then rose again to newness of life.

Note the two places for Calvary on the map. Also the two places for the Garden Tomb. Gordon's Calvary is at the top of the old city, to the north. The Garden Tomb which is nearby can be seen today. The place at the left is covered by the Church of the Holy Sepulchre.

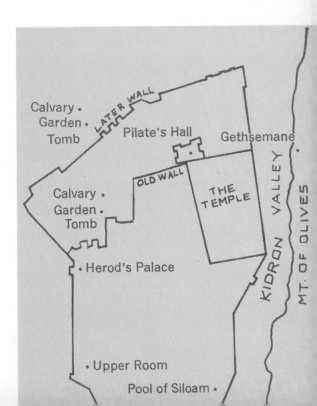

On the road to Emmaus,
Cleopas and his friend talked about
many strange things.

On the Road to Emmaus

Jesus appears to Cleopas
and another disciple

Mary Magdalene was certain that the disciples would believe her now. She had seen Jesus with her own eyes. She had heard Him with her own ears.

Her face filled with excitement, Mary hurried to the room where the disciples were still waiting. Her story flew from her lips. But Mary was the only one who was excited. By now the other women had come to think that they were wrong. Even Peter and John sat in doubt.

"It can't be," they kept saying. "We must not let our hopes rise."

"But I saw Him," Mary pleaded. "I touched Him and He talked with me."

But still no one would believe. It was too good to accept. They dared not let themselves believe it, then be bitterly disappointed again.

So through that strange Sunday, the disciples sat in the upper room and talked. They thought about all the wonderful things He had said and done. And they wondered about the things the women had told them.

The disciples were afraid to go out that day. They were sure that the religious leaders would start looking for them now that the Sabbath had ended. They would wait for a few days and then quietly slip back to Galilee.

As the day wore on, two of the disciples, Cleopas and a friend, decided they would try to leave. They lived at Emmaus, only eight miles away, so they would be home before dark. Saying goodbye to the other disciples, they slipped quietly into the streets and out through the city gates.

Once they were in the country, the two felt safe again. But even though they were safe, they were very, very sad.

"If only He could have become our king," one of them said. "What a wonderful king He could have been."

"Yes," said the other. "I cannot understand it. He almost became king when He rode into Jerusalem. Then He let the leaders crucify Him. Why? Couldn't He stop them?"

So the two talked as they walked along the road to Emmaus. Then suddenly, as if from nowhere, a Stranger was walking with them.

"What are you talking about?" the Stranger asked. "What makes you so sad today?"

Cleopas was surprised. "Are you the only visitor in Jerusalem who doesn't know the things that have happened?"

Quietly the Stranger asked, "What things?"

Cleopas wanted to talk with someone. So he told all that had happened in those days—how Jesus should have become King of

*Cleopas and his friend
begged the Stranger
to stay with them.*

Israel, but instead was crucified. He told how the women had discovered His tomb empty and how the disciples had talked all day about these things.

The Stranger listened until Cleopas could not find anything more to say. Then it was His turn to talk.

"Foolish people," He said. "You find it hard to believe, don't you?"

The two disciples were surprised at this scolding. But they knew it was true that all the disciples had found it hard to believe in those days.

The Stranger went on talking. "Jesus had to die like that and then go into His glory," He said.

Then the Stranger began to teach them the Scriptures about Jesus. From the very beginning, He told how Jesus was expected and how He had come. He helped them see clearly for the first time the wonderful plan that God had for His Son.

When the Stranger broke the bread,
Cleopas and his family and friends knew that it was Jesus.

122

By now the three had come to Emmaus. The Stranger said He was going farther, but Cleopas and his friend begged Him to stay with them. Perhaps He would teach them other things. They were beginning to see for the first time how God had planned for these things that were happening. They must know more.

"Stay with us," they begged. "It is almost evening. You should not walk farther now."

That evening, when the Stranger sat down to eat with Cleopas and his friend, He took the bread and thanked God for it. Then He broke the bread and gave it to them.

Suddenly Cleopas and his friend knew who the Stranger was. Why hadn't they seen this before? How could they not have recognized Him? "Jesus!" they said. But as soon as they recognized Him, He was gone. He had disappeared.

"Didn't our hearts burn inside while He talked to us on the road?" they asked each other. "Why didn't we know Him?"

As the two disciples talked, they realized that the news was too good to keep. They must go back to Jerusalem, this very night, back to the upper room, and tell their friends what they had seen.

Without waiting another minute, they hurried toward the city. How happy the others would be to know that the women had been right. Jesus was alive again. They had seen Him. These were two of the happiest men alive as they hurried to tell their friends the best news they had ever heard.

SOMETHING TO THINK ABOUT

1. If you had been Cleopas, would you have been excited? Would it have made you happy to see Jesus alive again?
2. When Cleopas and his friend had good news to tell about Jesus, what did they do? When you have good news to tell about Jesus, and you certainly do, what do you do? We should, like Cleopas, run to tell our friends about it.

EMMAUS

The village of Emmaus is mentioned only once in the entire Bible, in Luke 24: 13. Jesus had been crucified and had risen from the dead, but most of His disciples did not yet believe that He was alive. They were still meeting together in the Upper Room, although some of the women had visited the tomb on Sunday morning and found it empty. They had been told by an angel that Jesus had risen from the dead and had come back to the Upper Room to give the news to the other disciples. Peter and John came to the tomb and they found it empty, but they still were not sure. Then Jesus appeared to Mary Magdalene just outside the tomb.

Still not believing that Jesus was alive, Cleopas and a friend, two of the disciples, started home to Emmaus on Sunday night. On the way, they met a Stranger who told them many things about God's plans. When they reached home at Emmaus, they recognized that the Stranger was Jesus.

The picture on the opposite page shows some remains of an old Roman road. The location of this place is about two miles west of Gibeon, or about seven miles from Jerusalem. It is thought to be the place where the village of Emmaus stood in time of Christ.

This old Roman road may have been the same road over which Cleopas and his friend walked with Jesus.

The Bible says that Emmaus was sixty furlongs or stadia from Jerusalem. This would be about seven miles. But it does not say in which direction.

There have been many different opinions about Emmaus and its location. Some think it was at one place and some at another. The place where the above photo was taken is within seven miles of Jerusalem if the traveler walked on a path leading directly from the capital city to this village. Cleopas and his friend probably took this path or road which led directly home, and on this road they met Jesus.

About two miles to the east is the city of Gibeon, where Joshua commanded the sun to stand still (Joshua 10: 6-14).

When Weak Men Became Giants

Jesus appears to His disciples

It was getting dark, and the trip from Emmaus to Jerusalem was dangerous at night. But no matter how much danger faced them, Cleopas and his friend were determined to go back to tell the other disciples that they had seen Jesus.

The eight miles had never seemed so far before. But the two men ran as much as they could, more excited than they had ever been in their lives. Jesus, their Master, had risen from the dead. They knew now that He was the Messiah, the Lord of life, and they must tell the other disciples what had happened.

After what seemed the longest trip of their lives, the two disciples reached the upper room. Breathless, they hurried into the room to tell their story. But before they could say a word, the disciples began to tell them what had happened to them.

"The Lord appeared to Simon Peter today!" they said. "He is alive, we know it now."

Then Cleopas and his friend told all that had happened to them since they left earlier in the afternoon. Jesus was certainly alive, for they had seen Him, too.

126

Cleopas and his friend were more excited than they had ever been as they ran back to Jerusalem.

The disciples were all so busy talking that they didn't notice that Someone else had entered the room. Suddenly all talking stopped and a quiet hush fell over the room as one by one the disciples turned to see Him. It was Jesus.

"Peace be with you," Jesus said.

But the disciples were afraid. They had locked the doors and closed the windows. Jesus must have come right through the walls. Perhaps they were looking at His ghost. Perhaps He really wasn't alive after all.

Jesus knew their thoughts. He was sorry that they found it so hard to believe. "Why are you so troubled?" He asked. "Why do you keep questioning that I am alive? Touch my hands and my feet. Handle me and see that I have flesh and bones."

Carefully the disciples touched Him. They must know if He was real or not. But even when they touched Him, they still weren't

127

quite sure. They were so happy that they thought it was too good to be true.

Jesus must show them by some other way that He was alive. He must prove to them so there would never be doubts again.

"Do you have anything to eat?" He asked.

The disciples hurried around the room, looking for some food. There certainly wasn't much. They had not been able to buy much food since Jesus had been crucified. At last they found some broiled fish that someone had given them.

While the curious disciples watched, Jesus sat down and ate the food. There could be no doubt now. A ghost could not eat broiled fish. Jesus was a living Person again. He had risen from the dead.

When Jesus had finished eating, He began to teach the disciples what He had told Cleopas and his friend on the Emmaus road, starting with Moses and the prophets. One by one, Jesus showed them the many Scriptures that told of His coming.

"Thus it is written, that the Christ should suffer and on the third day rise from the dead," He said, "and that repentance and forgiveness of sins should be preached in His name to all nations. You are witnesses to these things."

Never before had the disciples seen so clearly how Jesus fit into God's wonderful plan. They had always thought of Him as a king for Israel, but they saw now that He must be King over all kings and all nations. And they would be His witnesses. His kingdom was far greater than all earthly kingdoms.

As they listened, the disciples felt their fear leaving them. They realized now what a wonderful honor God was giving to them. The group of weak, discouraged men was changing. They were becoming spiritual giants—men who would lead thousands to God through Jesus Christ.

128

SOMETHING TO THINK ABOUT

1. Have you ever thought about God's plans for your life? Why are you the person you are? Why did God make you the way He did? Many of these questions about ourselves can never be answered completely on this earth. But there are some parts of God's wonderful plan for us that we do know. The Bible tells us much about this plan. We know that God loves us very much (John 3: 16), that He does not want any of us to miss His great gift of eternal life (II Peter 3: 9), and that He has given the gift of eternal life to us through Jesus Christ (Romans 6: 23).

2. How do we know more about God's plans for our life? Here are some ways. First, we can read the Bible, for in it we learn what God has said. Second, we can pray, for by doing that, we bring ourselves in tune with God. Third, we can talk with others who know God through Christ, for they also have read the Bible and prayed and have much to share with us.

3. While it is important to know God's plans for us, there is something more important. What do you think that is? It is to follow God's plans when we know them. We must put hands and feet on the things we know are right.

4. One of the best ways to understand what God wants us to do is to start doing things for Him. He shows us His plans more clearly when we are walking closer to Him.

At last the disciples found some broiled fish for Jesus.

THE TWELVE DISCIPLES

Jesus had many disciples while He was on earth. But twelve were very close to Him, so they became known as "The Twelve Disciples." Later, after Jesus ascended into Heaven, they became known as apostles, along with Paul, who is sometimes called "the thirteenth apostle." These twelve, along with Paul, were probably the most important men who ever lived, for they carried on the work which Jesus Christ, the Son of God, began while He was on earth. The twelve were chosen by Jesus Himself.

PETER

A fisherman from Bethsaida. His name was Simon until Jesus named him Cephas, or Peter, which means "a stone" (John 1: 42). Peter became one of the leaders among the twelve and preached the important sermon at Pentecost which won thousands to Christ. Later he wrote I and II Peter.

ANDREW

Peter's brother. He was also a fisherman from Bethsaida. He was the man who brought his brother Simon (Peter) to Christ. He was also the man who found the boy with the loaves and fish which Jesus used to feed the five thousand.

JAMES

James and John were sons of Zebedee. These two and their father were in a fishing partnership with Peter and Andrew at Bethsaida. James was the first of the twelve to die when Herod killed him (Acts 12: 1, 2).

PHILIP

Philip was also from Bethsaida, the home town of Peter, Andrew, James, and John. When he found Christ, shortly after His temptation, he hurried to find Nathanael (Bartholomew) and bring him also to Christ (John 1: 45).

JOHN

John was a son of Zebedee and a brother of James. He must have known someone important in the high priest's household, for he was able to go inside when Jesus was tried. He wrote the Gospel of John; I, II, and III John; and Revelation.

130

BARTHOLOMEW

Nathanael or Bartholomew may have had a double name as we do today, Nathanael Bartholomew. When Philip brought him to Jesus, he was doubtful at first, but quickly saw that Jesus was the Son of God (John 1: 49).

MATTHEW

Also known as Levi. He was a tax collector, or publican, as they were sometimes called. Jesus called him to leave the tax office and follow Him. Matthew had to give up riches to be a disciple. Later he wrote the Book of Matthew.

SIMON THE ZEALOT

Simon was called a Cananaean in Matthew 10: 4. This was another word for Zealot (Luke 6: 15 and Acts 1: 13). Zealots were members of a Jewish patriotic party which wanted to overthrow the Romans and were willing to revolt to do it.

JUDAS ISCARIOT

Because of the way Judas betrayed Jesus, his name will always be hated. After Jesus showed that He would not be an earthly king, Judas agreed to betray Him for thirty pieces of silver, the price of a slave. Later, he threw the money back to the leaders (Matthew 27: 3-10) and hanged himself (Matthew 27: 5; Acts 1: 18).

THOMAS

Thomas will always be remembered as the doubter. He could not believe that Jesus had risen from the dead until he put his fingers into Jesus' scars. Then he believed (John 20: 28).

JAMES, SON OF ALPHAEUS

He was sometimes called "James the less" because he was less than the other apostle James or because he was shorter than the other apostles.

THADDAEUS

Two of the four lists of disciples give the name Thaddaeus (Matthew 10: 3, and Mark 3: 18). The other two lists give the name Judas instead, adding "son of James" which may have meant "brother of James" instead (Luke 6: 14-16 and Acts 1: 13). Thaddaeus has also been called Lebbaeus (Matthew 10: 3 in some versions).

131

Doubting Thomas

Jesus appears to Thomas

For some reason, Thomas was not with the disciples on that wonderful Sunday night when Jesus visited them in the upper room. Perhaps he was with other friends of Jesus to tell what had happened thus far. Or perhaps he was preparing to go back home.

Until Sunday night, when Jesus came to see the disciples, all of them had doubted that He was alive. They had called the women's story that morning "idle tales." They had not listened to Mary Magdalene, even when she had talked with Jesus.

When Peter, Cleopas, and the other disciple had seen Jesus they began to believe. But it was not until Jesus came into the upper room with the disciples that they were sure that He was alive.

Thomas had been gone that Sunday night, so he had not yet seen the risen Jesus.

"We have seen Jesus," the disciples told him when he returned. "We talked with Him. He ate some food in this very room."

"Idle tales," Thomas answered. "Like those the women told. Unless I see the scars in His hands and side and put my finger in them, I will not believe."

The days went by and Thomas kept on doubting. All week long he wondered why Jesus did not appear if He was really alive. The others said they saw Him. Were they wrong or was Jesus staying away from Thomas for some reason? Doubts nagged Thomas and made him feel terrible.

All during that week, the disciples waited in the upper room. Though they saw more clearly now what the Scriptures said about Jesus and understood at last how He fit into God's wonderful plan, they waited for Jesus to show them what to do. They simply didn't know how to get started.

Sunday came again, but no one had seen Jesus since last Sunday night. Where was He? What was He doing?

That evening, as the disciples talked with one another, they were startled to find Jesus standing with them in the upper room. The doors were locked, but He suddenly had appeared as though He had walked through the wall.

"Peace be unto you," said Jesus.

Thomas stared, almost refusing to believe his eyes. But it was Jesus and he could no longer doubt. The other disciples had not imagined it. They were right.

Jesus was not looking at the other disciples. He was looking at Thomas.

"Put your finger here in My scars, Thomas," Jesus said to him. "Stop doubting and start believing."

Thomas was so ashamed. Jesus knew all his thoughts. No one had told Him. Now he didn't want to touch those wonderful scars. He felt sorry because of his doubts. How could he have doubted like that?

But Jesus guided Thomas' finger into the scars that had been made at Golgotha. No longer could there be any doubt. Thomas fell to the floor before Jesus.

"My Lord and my God," he whispered. At last Thomas felt happy again. His doubts were gone.

"Thomas," Jesus answered, "have you believed because you have seen Me? Blessed are those who have not seen and yet believe."

Jesus must have been looking across the years at all the other "doubting Thomases" who can't believe because they can't see Him. But He was also thinking of the hundreds of thousands who believe in Him whom they have never seen.

SOMETHING TO THINK ABOUT

1. What does it mean to doubt? When we doubt, do we have any questions about our belief? Or, are we just not quite sure that our belief is true?
2. Thomas had doubts. He could not bring himself to believe that Jesus had risen from the dead. But Thomas was not the only disciple who had doubts about Jesus' resurrection at first. Almost all of the disciples had doubts the morning when Jesus rose and the women went to find His tomb empty.
3. All people have doubts at some time. It's not always bad to have doubts, but it is very bad to keep them. John the Baptist had doubts about Jesus, so he tried to find out the truth about Jesus (Luke 7: 18-30). Jesus praised John as the greatest of men. He did not hold John's doubts against him.
4. What should we do when we have doubts? Like John the Baptist, let's go to Jesus. John couldn't go himself, for he was in prison, so he sent some friends. But we can always go to Jesus for help. Let's go to the Bible to find answers for our doubts. The Bible has all the answers for our questions about God and His relationship to us. Let's also go to our friends who know God and talk over our doubts with them. Perhaps they have had the same doubts but found answers to them. But make sure you talk with friends who have learned God's answers, not the answers of the godless. Friends who don't know God can often make our doubts worse if we listen to them.
5. Why do you think John the Baptist had doubts (Luke 7: 18-30)? Remember that John was in prison and could not be with Jesus. That's when doubts begin to come—when we are not walking with Jesus. If we walk close to Him each day, we will not have doubts so easily. Let's remember to read our Bibles and pray each day. That's the best way to keep doubts away.

"Put your finger in My scars, Thomas, and start believing," Jesus said.

135

CHAPTERS FROM

If a "Life of Thomas" had been written, here are some of the chapter headings you might find in it.

THE LIFE
of
DOUBTING
THOMAS

CHAPTER 1
JOINING UP WITH JESUS

Thomas is called to be one of Jesus' disciples.
Matthew 10: 3, Mark 3: 18, Luke 6: 15

CHAPTER 2
THE FEARLESS FOLLOWER

When Lazarus dies, Thomas urges the other disciples to go with Jesus to Bethany, where there are many enemies of Jesus.
John 11: 16

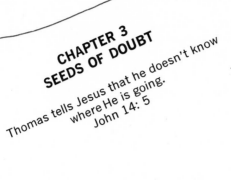

CHAPTER 3
SEEDS OF DOUBT

Thomas tells Jesus that he doesn't know
where He is going.
John 14: 5

CHAPTER 4
THE MISSING DISCIPLE

Thomas leaves the disciples for a while.
John 20: 24

CHAPTER 5
THE SCARS HE HAD TO TOUCH

Thomas touches the scars on Jesus' hands
and side. Then he believes.
John 20: 27, 28

CHAPTER 6
WAITING IN THE FISHING BOAT

Thomas goes fishing with some other
disciples as they wait for Jesus in Galilee.
John 21: 1-25

137

Home to Galilee

Jesus appears to the disciples in Galilee

Never in their lives had the disciples been so glad to start home to Galilee. Their days in Jerusalem had been a nightmare. Since Jesus had been captured in Gethsemane, they had known nothing but fear. Even though Jesus had risen from the dead, the disciples still feared that the leaders would try to put Him to death again.

So when the Passover ended, the disciples joined the thousands of travelers headed back to their homes. The roads were crowded with people, talking and arguing about the things that had happened.

Some argued that Jesus deserved to die. Others were sad that He had not become the King of Israel. But all wondered about the things they had heard—the empty tomb and the stories that the disciples had stolen His body.

Anxious to get home, the disciples didn't stop to tell these people what had really happened. They wouldn't believe it anyway. If they made themselves known, the religious leaders might put them to death.

How lonely the familiar roads to home seemed now without Jesus. For three years they had walked with Him. Now everything

138

seemed so different. They felt alone and confused. What did Jesus want them to do? Where did He want them to go? The angel had said He would meet them in Galilee. But where? And when would that happen?

But their anxious feelings began to disappear as they came over the top of a hill and saw their beloved town of Capernaum lying in the distance. The blue waters of the Sea of Galilee nearby looked more beautiful than ever before. For years they had fished on these waters. It was all part of home.

"I know what I'm going to do," Peter said. "I'm going fishing."

The idea caught hold at once. What a wonderful thought! While they waited for Jesus, they would go back to the old familiar things—the boats, the nets, and the beautiful waters of the sea.

By the time the disciples had prepared the net and the boat, it was sundown. The gentle evening breeze caught their sail and carried them out over the water. In the west, the colors of the sunset brought a strange peace that they had not known for many days. How they longed for Jesus to be with them.

Again and again the disciples cast their net into the sea. But each time they pulled it in the net was empty.

Night came and the stars twinkled in the sky. Time after time, the big net splashed into the dark waters. But always it came back empty.

So it went all night long. How many times they must have thrown that net into the water during the long hours of the night. But not one fish was pulled in. By morning the disciples were very discouraged.

"Let's throw it in a few more times," one of them said. "If we get nothing, we'll go home."

The others agreed. Fishing wouldn't be much good when daylight came.

But even as they picked up the net to throw it in, they heard a voice calling from shore. Turning to see who had spoken, they noticed a Stranger standing by the sea.

"Have you caught anything?" the Stranger asked.

"No, nothing," they answered.

"Then throw your net on the right side of the boat," the Stranger called back.

The disciples looked at each other. Should they do it? Who was this Man to tell them what to do? But it was worth a try. Perhaps He knew something they didn't.

With one last effort, the disciples threw the net into the sea on the right side of the boat. Suddenly the sea became alive with silver streaks below the water.

"Look!" shouted one of the disciples. "Fish! Dozens of them!"

"The net is full of fish," shouted another disciple. "Quick, haul them in."

Time after time the big net splashed
into the dark waters.
But always it came back empty.

"I can't," shouted another. "It's too full. I can't get it into the boat."

By now John had begun to wonder about the Stranger standing on shore. He remembered another time when they had fished all night without catching anything. Someone had helped them then.

"Peter," John whispered. "It's the Lord!"

Peter looked again at the Man standing alone on the shore. It *was* Jesus! He could see clearly now. Jesus had come to Galilee, as He had promised.

SOMETHING TO THINK ABOUT

1. Jesus had promised His disciples that He would come to Galilee to be with them. Did He keep that promise? Does Jesus always keep His promises?
2. Do you always keep your promises to Him? A promise is a down payment on an action, isn't it? When we promise to do something, we should always follow through.
3. Ecclesiastes 5: 4 tells us that it is better not to promise than to promise and then fail to do what we said. Does that mean that we should never promise God anything? God wouldn't want that, would He? No, we should promise God our best, but we should be sure to give it.

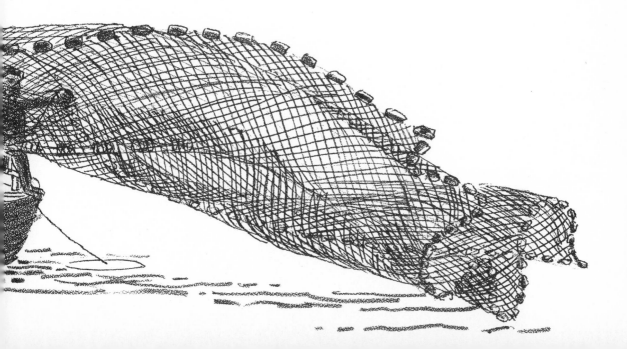

DID ANYONE SEE JESUS ALIVE?

WHO? WHERE? WHEN?

Many saw Jesus die. Some saw Him buried. But did anyone see Him alive after His crucifixion? What does the Bible tell us?

The Bible says that there were many people who saw Him alive after His death. Here is a list of some of those people, with the places and times when they saw Him. Look up each Scripture and read the story.

1. Who: Mary Magdalene,
Mary, Salome
Where: Jesus' Tomb Outside
Jerusalem
When: Early Sunday morning
Which Scripture:
Matthew 28: 9, 10

2. Who: Peter
Where: Jesus' Tomb outside
Jerusalem
When: Sunday morning
Which Scriptures:
Luke 24: 33-35; I Cor. 15: 5

3. Who: Mary Magdalene
Where: Jesus' Tomb outside Jerusalem
When: Sunday morning
Which Scripture:
John 20: 11-18

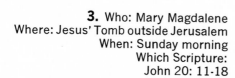

4. Who: Cleopas and another
disciple
Where: Emmaus and a
nearby road
When: Sunday evening
Which Scriptures:
Mark 16: 12, 13;
Luke 24: 13-32

5. Who: Ten Apostles—Thomas absent
Where: Upper room, Jerusalem
When: Sunday night
Which Scriptures:
Mark 16: 14; Luke 24: 36-43;
John 20: 19-25

6. Who: Eleven Apostles,
including Thomas
Where: Upper room,
Jerusalem
When: The next Sunday
Which Scriptures:
John 20: 26-31;
I Cor. 15: 5

7. Who: Peter, Thomas, Nathanael,
James, John, and two other disciples
Where: Sea of Galilee
When: Not known
Which Scripture:
John 21

8. Who: Eleven Apostles, then
five-hundred
Where: A mountain in
Galilee
When: Not known
Which Scriptures:
Mark 16: 15-18; Matt. 28:
16-20; I Cor. 15: 6

9. Who: James
Where: Not known
When: Not known
Which Scripture:
I Cor. 15: 7

10. Who: Eleven Apostles
Where: Mt. of Olives, near
Bethany
When: Day of Ascension
Which Scriptures:
Mark 16: 19, 20;
Luke 24: 44-53; Acts 1: 3-12

11. Who: Saul (Paul)
Where: Road near
Damascus
When: Not known
Which Scripture:
Acts 9: 1-9

Feed My Sheep

Jesus talks with Peter

The disciples were so happy to see Jesus standing on the shore of the Sea of Galilee. He had come home to be with them, as the angel had promised.

Peter couldn't wait until they brought the boat to shore, so he jumped into the water, and headed for shore.

The water was shallow here, so Peter waded through the sea until he came to Jesus. How happy he was to see Jesus here in the old familiar places.

Dragging the heavy net full of fish, the other disciples brought the boat to shore. For a few minutes there was nothing but happy talk as the disciples and Jesus met together again.

At last Jesus pointed toward a warm fire He had made on the shore. "Bring some of the fish you have caught," He said. The disciples noticed then that there was bread toasting on the fire.

Peter didn't wait for another word. Quickly he helped to drag the heavy net onto the shore. The disciples began to count the fish. When they finished, they had a hundred and fifty-three fish.

"Come and have breakfast," Jesus told His friends.

What a wonderful breakfast that was—fresh fish and toast, roasted on a charcoal fire along the Sea of Galilee.

When breakfast was over, Jesus stepped to one side with Peter. Jesus pointed to the boat, the nets, and the fish.

"Simon," He said, "do you love Me more than these?"

Peter was surprised and a little hurt that Jesus would ask such a question. Of course he loved Jesus more than all the boats and nets in the world.

"You know that I love you, Lord," Peter answered meekly.

The disciples were so happy to see Jesus standing on the shore.
He had come to Galilee to meet them, just as He had promised.

"Feed My sheep," Jesus told Peter.

Jesus looked at Peter in a way the fisherman had never seen before. It was a commanding look.

"Feed My lambs," Jesus said.

Peter was puzzled. What did Jesus mean?

Then Jesus asked Peter a second time, "Simon, do you love Me?"

146

Peter was more puzzled than ever. He had just told Jesus that he loved Him. What did Jesus want?

But Peter answered the best he knew how. "Lord, You know that I love You," he said again.

Then Jesus spoke very quietly to Peter. Peter knew now that Jesus wanted something very much.

"Take care of My sheep, Simon," He said.

Peter wanted so much to please Jesus. But he wasn't sure what Jesus was telling him. But before he could ask, Jesus spoke again.

"Simon, do You really love Me?" He asked.

By now, Peter felt very sad about this talk. Why did Jesus keep asking him? Didn't Jesus think Peter loved Him? Peter thought of that terrible night in the courtyard when he had cursed and denied that he knew Jesus. Perhaps that was why Jesus kept asking if he loved Him.

"Lord, You know everything," Peter said quickly. "You know that I love You."

It was true. Jesus did know everything. He knew Peter well enough to know that the fisherman did love Him, even though he had denied Him.

"Then feed My sheep," Jesus told him.

Peter didn't understand that morning what Jesus was saying. But later he came to realize who those sheep were. Jesus wanted Peter and the other disciples to take care of His followers—His sheep. Peter and his friends would feed them—they would help others know God's Word, they would pray with them, talk with them, and would help them grow stronger as believers in Jesus.

Peter never forgot those words that Jesus spoke that morning on Galilee's shore. The Good Shepherd was going soon to be with His Father in Heaven. If His sheep were to be fed and cared for, the disciples must do it. He had no one else to do His work.

KINDS OF LOVE

The Bible speaks of many kinds of love. Each kind is important, for it is different from the other kinds. Look up the Scripture references. They will help you understand more about the different kinds of love.

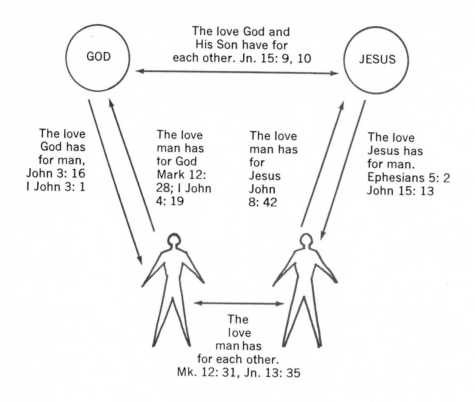

The New Testament, written originally in Greek, uses two different words for love.

AGAPE

This word means to choose to love someone or something. The person has thought it through and has decided to do it. It is more of a "head" love.

PHILEO

This word means to love someone or something more emotionally. It is a warmer, more sentimental love. It is more of a "heart" love.

In this story, Jesus said, "Do you AGAPE Me?" Peter answered, "I PHILEO you." Jesus asked the same question again and Peter answered the same. Then Jesus asked, "Do you really PHILEO Me?" Peter was hurt, but said "yes."

Beyond the Clouds

Jesus rises into Heaven

For forty days Jesus appeared now and then to His disciples. Sometimes He taught them. At other times He showed them that He was truly alive. Never again should there be a question about His resurrection. Never again should anyone doubt that He rose from the dead.

Sometime during these forty days, Jesus made arrangements for His eleven special friends to meet Him in Jerusalem. They dreaded the thought of going back to Jerusalem, but they knew now they would go anywhere He asked.

When the time came, the disciples went to the place He had told them, probably the upper room where they had eaten the Last Supper together. There they listened as He told them many wonderful things about His work.

"Wait here in Jerusalem," He said. "The Promise of the Father will come to you. When that happens, you will be baptized with the Holy Spirit."

The disciples could not understand what Jesus meant. How would they be baptized with the Holy Spirit? What would happen? When would this take place?

While they wondered about these things, they walked with Him

Jesus began to rise from the earth,
moving higher and higher toward Heaven.

150

through the city streets, down the familiar paths into the Kidron Valley, and up the Mount of Olives. They couldn't help but think of the last time they were here—that night when the soldiers came to take Jesus away to be crucified.

As they walked past the Garden of Gethsemane, all was quiet now among the olive trees. It was the picture of peace. There were no soldiers or guards now, only the sweet song of birds among the olive branches.

But Jesus did not stop in the Garden of Gethsemane. Instead, He walked toward the top of the Mount of Olives, on the way to Bethany.

"Will you now help our nation get free from the Romans?" some asked Him.

Kindly but firmly, Jesus spoke to them. "It is not for you to know what God will do and at what time," He said. "God has decided these things, but He will not tell you."

Then Jesus looked around at His friends. "When the Holy Spirit comes upon you, you will receive power," He said. "Then you will go everywhere telling people about Me, even to the ends of the earth."

The disciples wanted to ask Jesus more about this, but even as they wondered what to say, Jesus began to rise from the ground. He had said He would go back to His Father in Heaven, but somehow they had not expected this.

Higher and higher Jesus rose into the air. At last He went beyond the clouds and they saw Him no more.

But the disciples could not move. They stood still, looking and looking for some sign of Him.

While they stood watching the sky, voices spoke behind them. Turning quickly, they saw two strangers dressed in white.

"Men of Galilee," the strangers said, "why are you standing here,

151

looking up into Heaven? This same Jesus, who has gone from you into Heaven, will come again some day in the same way that you have seen Him leave."

Then the disciples knew who the strangers were. They were angels, sent from God to tell them this wonderful news.

Slowly the disciples turned and walked down to Jerusalem again. Jesus had said to wait there for the Holy Spirit to come. What would happen, they did not know. But they knew that they would do anything for Jesus, even wait again in the upper room.

SOMETHING TO THINK ABOUT

1. What would you think of following Christ if you could visit His grave and read His tombstone? Would you believe Him when He said, "I am the resurrection and the life" (John 11:25)? Would you believe it was true? Would you believe Him when He said, "I am the way, the truth, and the life. No man can come to the Father except through Me" (John 14:6)? Would you trust a dead Jesus to take you to Heaven?

2. But Jesus is alive. He is living in Heaven, where He is preparing a place for us. Men saw Him alive after He was crucified. The disciples saw Him rise from the earth and go toward Heaven. Do you think they believed that He could take them to Heaven, too? Of course they did.

3. Jesus is not only alive in Heaven, but He is coming back to get us some day. The angels told this to the disciples as they watched Jesus rise. Jesus will take His followers back to be with Him in His home forever.

4. What would you have done if you had seen Jesus crucified, then had been with Him after He rose from the dead, then seen Him rise up into Heaven? Would you have believed in Him? Would you have told others about Him? But you know these things have happened, for the Bible tells us about them. Should you do any less than you would have done if you had been with Him?

5. Is Jesus alive today? The Bible tells us that He is. We have a living Savior. How can you refuse to accept the living Son of God into your life? If you haven't, do it now.

152

From the Temple area in Jerusalem, one can look across the Kidron Valley to the Mount of Olives.

THE MOUNT OF OLIVES

Only a short distance to the east of Jerusalem rises a large hill on which olive trees still grow. This is called the Mount of Olives. On this mount, Jesus began his Triumphal Entry into Jerusalem (Matthew 21: 1-11, 14-17; Mark 11: 1-11; Luke 19: 28-44; John 11: 55–12: 1, 12-19; see pages 20 to 25 of this volume). Here, He also prayed in the Garden of Gethsemane (Matthew 26: 30-56; Mark 14: 26-52; Luke 22: 39-53; John 18: 1-12; see pages 64 to 73 of this volume). From this mount Jesus also ascended into Heaven. The disciples watched Him leave, then walked back into Jerusalem to wait for the coming of the Holy Spirit.

One Voice
but Many Voices

The disciples pray in the upper room

No one knew exactly how long the disciples stood on the Mount of Olives, watching Jesus rise up into the sky. No one dared to guess. But it must have been for a long time. Not one disciple was in a hurry to leave.

There was something very strange and very wonderful about the way Jesus had gone. The disciples had heard Jesus say that He would return to Heaven to be with His Father. But somehow they had never quite expected His return to be this way. They had never been quite sure what to expect.

But now He was gone. They were sure of that. With their own eyes, the disciples had seen His feet leave the ground in that wonderful place. With their own eyes they had watched Him rise up through the clouds and disappear into the heavens. No one could ever convince them that Jesus had not risen. They had seen Him go.

But now that Jesus was gone, the disciples felt helpless and alone. They weren't sure what they should do or where they should go. Jesus had said something about the Holy Spirit coming to be

154

Like sheep looking for a shepherd,
the disciples left the Mount of Olives for Jerusalem.

with them, but they didn't know when He would come or in what way. They weren't sure how they would recognize the Holy Spirit when He did come.

Everything seemed so strange and lonely as the disciples stood quietly on the Mount of Olives. If only Jesus were back, He would know what to do. Occasionally one of them would look back into the sky, trying to catch some glimpse of Jesus. But they saw nothing.

At last, after what seemed an endless time, one of the disciples broke the silence. "I'm going back to the upper room," he said. "That's what Jesus wanted us to do."

The disciple turned and started down the slope of the Mount of Olives, headed toward Jerusalem. Soon another disciple came behind him, then another and another. Like sheep looking for a shepherd, they all began to follow, down through the Kidron Valley and up again toward the great gate that led into the city.

The disciples hardly noticed the noise of the city streets as they made their way to the upper room where they had eaten the Last

155

Supper with Jesus. The cries of the merchants and the rumbling of the ox carts meant nothing to them today. They had only one thought—to be together in the upper room.

But when the disciples came into the upper room, they still didn't know what to do. Jesus had said to wait for His Promise, but what should they do while they were waiting?

Suddenly one of the disciples bowed his head and began to pray. It seemed the right thing to do. When he finished, another began to pray, too. Then another followed him.

What a prayer meeting that was! Never had these people felt so close to God! Never had they felt so close to each other!

One day, as the disciples were praying, they heard a strange noise. It sounded like wind blowing through the room. They stopped praying to see what was happening.

"Look!" one of them whispered. "There's a little flame of fire on you."

"There's one on you, too," said another. The disciples looked around the room. There was a flame of fire on each one there.

"Could this be what Jesus promised?" they asked.

It *was* what Jesus had promised. The Holy Spirit had come upon the disciples. Their lives would never be the same again.

SOMETHING TO THINK ABOUT

1. Why do you think the disciples prayed while they waited? Why didn't they play games or have a party? They all wanted very much for God to show them what to do, didn't they? Is prayer a good way for us to learn more about God's plans for us? It's one good way, isn't it? Can you think of others?
2. What happened when the disciples prayed? How did they feel toward each other? Prayer does this. That's why it's good to pray with other believers.
3. The Holy Spirit changed the lives of the believers. Can He change yours also? He will if you will let Him.

156

As the disciples prayed in the upper room,
it seemed that God was there with them.

3. Prayer makes us happy, too. Can you think why we are happier when we pray? Are we happier when we are near God? Are we happier when we please God? Try praying. You'll find that you are a happier person as you pray more.
4. Prayer kept the disciples from putting themselves first. It's hard to put self first when we pray, isn't it? If we do, we're not really seeking God's will.

157

WHO WROTE THE BOOK OF ACTS?

The Book of Acts was written by Luke, the same man who wrote The Gospel According to Luke.

Luke was a physician. Sometimes he is called the "beloved physician" because Paul called him that (Colossians 4:14). We get the thought from this that Luke was a kind-hearted doctor who was very tender with his patients and with others.

But Luke fell in love with another kind of work. When he became a believer in Christ, he began to work with Paul as a missionary (Acts 16:10-17; 20:5-15; 21:1-18; and 27:1—28:16 show that he was with Paul, for he spoke as "we").

Not only was Luke the world's first missionary doctor, but he was also a great writer. His writing in the Book of Luke and the Book of Acts shows skill in this art.

Luke is mentioned in Colossians 4:14, Philemon 24, and II Timothy 4:11. Philemon 24 shows that Luke kept on working with Paul, for he was still with Paul when the Book of Philemon was written, while Paul was waiting for his trial in Rome.

When Paul wrote II Timothy 4:11, he was probably in jail in Rome, waiting to be put to death. Almost all his friends had left him by now. But one person stayed behind with him—Luke the beloved physician. No wonder Paul called him that!

Luke was probably not a Jew, like Paul, but a Gentile. Paul may have won him to Christ in one of his missionary journeys. Some think that Luke was a Macedonian and may well have been the man in Paul's vision, the man who said, "come over to Macedonia and help us." He was probably from Philippi.

Of the four men who wrote the Gospels, Matthew and John were apostles and Mark and Luke were not. But Luke was the only Gentile and the only one born and raised outside the land of Israel.

The Gospel of Luke and The Book of Acts were written by Doctor Luke, the world's first medical missionary.

The people felt very strange
as Peter preached.

160

A City That Found Its Soul

Peter preaches at Pentecost

Foreign people all over Jerusalem were amazed. Common, ordinary Galileans were talking to them in their own languages. The Galileans were telling these visitors about Jesus, talking as though they had known their strange languages all their lives.

"How can this be?" some of the people asked. "They're talking in languages they could never have learned."

Some of the people who did not like the disciples were angry. "They are drunk," these people said.

Peter stood up before the crowds of people. "Listen to me, all of you. These people are not drunk. You should know that!"

The people gathered closer to hear what Peter had to say. "This was told by the prophet many years ago," said Peter. "God told of a day when He would pour out His Spirit on men and they would say great things for Him."

The people listened carefully. They could see now that Peter was certainly not drunk. They had never heard a man speak so well —except Jesus.

"In that day," said Peter, "anyone who calls upon the name of the Lord will be saved. Whoever asks God to give him a life that goes on forever will get it."

Some of the people felt strange as Peter went on talking. They felt as if God had told this man what to say. It had been many years since there had been a prophet in Israel. But this man was speaking boldly, like a prophet. They listened even more carefully now as he spoke.

"God sent His Son Jesus among you to show you signs and wonderful things. What did you do? You crucified Him. You killed the Son of God."

The people groaned. Could this be true? Could they really have crucified God's Son? What had they done? What would God do to them?

"But God raised Jesus from the dead and made Him alive again," said Peter. "We saw Him alive. We know that He lives today and has gone back to God, where He sits at God's right hand."

"What have we done? What have we done?" cried many of the people. They covered their faces. They felt so ashamed that they had done this terrible thing. If only God would spare them and not punish them for killing His only Son. "What can we do?" they cried out to Peter and the other eleven followers of Jesus.

"You must be sorry that you have done this wicked thing," said Peter. "You must turn away from the evil you have done and ask God to forgive you. Be baptized in the name of Jesus Christ so He can forgive your sins. Then God will send His Spirit upon you as He did upon us."

From all over the crowds of people men and women began to come closer to the followers of Christ. "We want God to forgive us," they said. "We want to be baptized."

More and more people kept crowding around the disciples. Hundreds of people begged to be baptized so they could follow Je-

162

sus. Never had the disciples seen anything like this! They could hardly believe it was happening.

At last, the disciples had finished baptizing the people. There had been over three thousand! The tiny group of a hundred and twenty disciples had grown almost thirty times that day.

Things began to happen in Jerusalem now. The followers of Jesus met to pray and talk about Jesus. Each day more and more asked to be baptized so they could show that they were following Jesus, too.

Jerusalem had crucified Jesus. But now Jerusalem had found its soul. Thousands were beginning to feel sorry for what they had done to God's Son. They were sorry that they had not stopped the leaders from killing Him. They had let Him die.

To the disciples, nothing seemed more wonderful than to see all of these people giving themselves to God so they could become Jesus' followers. "Surely God is working in a mighty way," they said. "We know now that His Promise, the Holy Spirit, has come to work with us, for we could never do these things ourselves."

"What have we done?" the people cried out.
They felt so ashamed that they had killed the Son of God.

WHAT WAS PENTECOST?

Once each year, the Jewish people had a special feast called Pentecost. Sometimes it was called the Feast of Weeks (Exodus 34: 22, Deuteronomy 16: 9-11), the Day of First Fruits (Numbers 28: 26), or the Feast of Harvest (Exodus 23: 16).

The word Pentecost meant "the fiftieth day," for it was held on the fiftieth day after the Feast of the Passover.

Pentecost was sometimes called the Day of First Fruits because the first part of the wheat harvest was brought to it. There the grain was given to God as a token of thanks for His goodness in the harvest. Because the wheat harvest was the last of the grain to be harvested each year, this feast closed the harvest season. It would have been similar to our thanksgiving.

No work was to be done during Pentecost. Every man and boy in Israel was to go to God's house, the Temple.

Not only was the grain to be brought to the Lord, but also an offering of two loaves of bread, seven one-year-old lambs, a young bull, two rams, and one male goat.

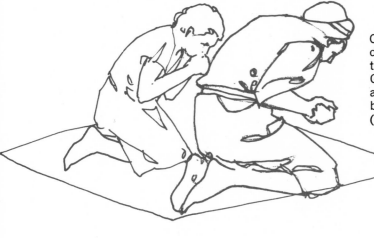

On the Pentecost when the disciples met in the upper room, the Holy Spirit came upon them. God visited His people in fire again, just as He had done in the burning bush.
(Exodus 3: 2).

The Jewish Pentecost was a harvest festival. But for the Christians, it was a harvest of harvests, for three thousand new people were gathered into the young church when Peter preached his great sermon.

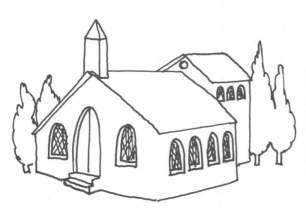

Some churches today celebrate Whitsuntide or Whitsunday, fifty days after Easter. It is a day to remember the coming of the Holy Spirit to earth.

Because many wore white robes on this day, it came to be called Whitsunday.

165

The Man Who Leaped and Jumped

Peter heals a lame man

It was no fun to sit there by the Beautiful Gate of the Temple all the time. Every day the poor man came, carried to the Temple gate by some friends. It was the only way he could get there, for he was a cripple. He never could walk, for he had been born that way.

All day long the lame man sat, begging for money. Whenever someone came in or out of the Temple, the lame man asked him for some money. "Please help me," he begged. "I can't walk. So I can't work like you can."

Some people tossed a few coins to him as they walked by. He always smiled and thanked them for the money, but very few bothered to smile back. Without those few coins, the man would have no money to buy food and clothing.

One day Peter and John walked toward the Temple. They wanted to pray to God. In the quietness of the beautiful Temple, they could pray and listen to Him.

As the two men walked up to the Beautiful Gate, a voice called to them. "Give a poor beggar some money!" the voice cried out. "Please help me."

166

"Get up and walk!"
Peter told the crippled man.

Peter and John stopped. They walked over to the lame man. When they looked at the poor man, they felt very sorry for him. How sad it would be to have to sit and beg all day—every day.

The man smiled as Peter and John walked toward him. These men had kind faces. Perhaps they would give him some money. Or perhaps they would say a kind word to him.

167

"I have no money either," Peter told the man. The poor man's face became sad again. But then he looked up into Peter's face. Peter was smiling at him.

"I will give you something that I do have," Peter said. "In the name of Jesus Christ of Nazareth, get up and walk!"

The man was stunned by Peter's words. What was he saying? How could this kind man say such a thing? Couldn't he see that he was a cripple?

Then Peter reached down and took the man by his hand. The man reached his hand toward Peter.

Slowly, Peter lifted the man to his feet. He began to wobble at first, then suddenly he stood tall and straight, like other men.

"Praise God!" shouted the man. "I'm standing! I'm standing!" Then, without stopping to think that he had never walked before, he began leaping and jumping all around the gate. As he leaped and jumped, he kept shouting, "Praise God! I can walk!" What a happy, exciting time that was!

When Peter and John walked into the Temple, the man ran in with them, leaping and jumping all the time. People began to stare at this man jumping around. What was he doing?

Then the people saw who it was. It was the lame man who had sat by the Beautiful Gate. But now he was walking, and jumping, and running.

The man was so excited
he began jumping
and shouting.

168

The people were all amazed. What had happened? How could this crippled man be jumping around like that?

Others ran over to see the strange sight. They stood around Peter and John and the man who had been healed, staring at them.

"It *is* the lame man," some whispered. "But now he is healed. What happened?"

"How should I know?" whispered another. "It's a miracle."

The other people agreed. It was certainly a miracle! Never before had they seen such a thing. So they stared all the more at the lame man and the two who had made him well.

THE BOOK OF ACTS

AND HEROD'S TEMPLE

Some events in the Book of Acts took place in Herod's Temple. To find where each event took place, locate the matching number for the event on the diagram on the facing page.

1. PETER'S GREAT SERMON. The Bible does not say where Peter preached this sermon, but it is likely that he was in the Court of the Gentiles at the Temple. This was the gathering place for many people. Also, we know that Peter and the other disciples went to the Temple daily. Acts 2. See Vol. 8, pp. 160-165.

2. PETER HEALS A LAME MAN. Entering the Temple area known as the Treasury, or the Court of Women, Peter and John were going through the Beautiful Gate, facing the east. There they saw a lame man and Peter healed him. Acts 3: 1-11. See Vol. 8, pp. 166-171.

3. PETER PREACHES AND HEALS ON SOLOMON'S PORCH. The disciples were meeting now on the open porch on the eastern side of the Temple, known as Solomon's porch. People brought the sick so Peter could heal them. The jealous high priest had the disciples arrested and thrown into prison, but the angel of God released them and sent them back to the Temple to preach. Acts 5: 12-42. See Vol. 8, pp. 178-185.

4. PAUL PREACHES IN THE TEMPLE. After Paul's third missionary journey, he returned to Jerusalem and entered the Temple to make a sacrifice. But some of his enemies saw him and started a riot. Paul was arrested and taken to the Tower of Antonia, the Roman fortress. On the steps of this building, Paul preached to the people. Acts 21: 16—23: 10. See Vol. 9, pp. 138-145.

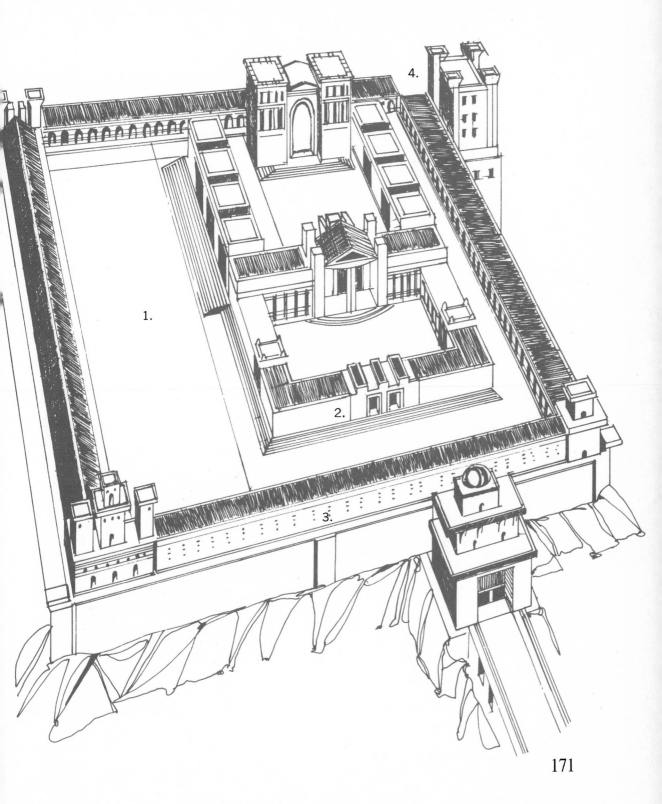

171

The Man Who Lied to God

Ananias and Sapphira

Whenever someone became a disciple and joined the early church, he shared what he owned with the others. The poor disciples were very happy. They had never had anyone do that before. They often talked with their friends about the kind things the new disciples were doing.

"Did you know that the rich man who became a disciple gave all his money to Peter to help the others?" some might say.

"Yes," said others. "He must be a very kind person to do that."

So the men who shared their riches became very popular. People said many wonderful things about them.

There were two new disciples, Ananias and Sapphira, who had some land. They knew what good things the others were saying about those who shared. So this couple decided on a plan. They wanted the others to say good things about them, too. They would do something about it.

Ananias and Sapphira sold their land. They put some of their money in a little bag. They would give that to the disciples. But they put most of their money in a big bag. They would keep that for

172

"This is our secret," Ananias told Sapphira.
"No one else will ever know."

themselves. They would tell the disciples that they were giving everything they had.

"What will the disciples think if they find out?" Sapphira asked her husband Ananias.

"They'll never know," Ananias smiled. "This is our secret. We can keep our money and get the honor, too!"

"You're so smart!" Sapphira whispered. "When will you take this little bag of money to Peter?"

"Now," said Ananias. He picked up the small bag of money and hurried down the street to find Peter.

"We've sold our land," he told Peter. "We want to give all our money so you can share it with the disciples."

"All your money, Ananias?" Peter asked. "Why are you lying like this? You know this is not all your money. You could give anything you want to give, but you must never lie to God."

Ananias was terrified. God knew about his plan. Peter knew,

173

too. Now all the disciples would find out. What would they think of him? They would never say good things about him. They would say terrible things about him.

Suddenly Ananias felt very strange. Then he fell on the floor. "He's dead," said Peter. "Would some of you young men carry him out and bury him?"

About three hours later, Sapphira came into the room. "Tell me," asked Peter, "did you sell your land for so much?" Sapphira knew how much money Ananias had brought to Peter. It was the amount Peter had said. "Yes, yes," she said, "that's what we got for it."

Peter looked at Sapphira. "How could you do this? You and your husband both agreed to lie to God about this money. The young men who have just buried your husband will take you out to bury you, too."

Sapphira could not even answer. She fell quietly to the floor and died. So the young men carried Sapphira out and buried her beside Ananias.

When the other disciples heard about Ananias and Sapphira, they were afraid. They knew then that no man can lie to God. "Oh, God," they prayed. "Help us always to tell the truth to You."

SOMETHING TO THINK ABOUT

1. What does it mean to tell a lie? Are we lying when we say something that isn't true? Are we lying when we pretend to be someone or something which we are not?
2. There are many ways to lie. If a man wore a policeman's uniform, but he wasn't a policeman, would he be lying? What if a man pretended to be a Christian, but he really wasn't? Would he be lying? Do we have to say all our lies or can we live some of them?
3. When we lie, who do we hurt most? Sometimes we hurt the other person, especially if the lie is against him. But more than that, we hurt

"Why are you lying to God about your money?" Peter asked Ananias.

ourselves, for lying robs us of our best self. It stains our good character and makes us think less of ourselves. It makes others think less of us, too. How can people trust the word of a person who lies to them? Can you?

4. Is there such a thing as a little lie or a big lie? Sometimes little lies have big troubles come from them.

5. Can we lie by doing nothing when we should do something? Read James 4: 17. Lying separates us from God. That is the worst result of all.

175

WHAT THE BOOK OF ACTS SAYS ABOUT PETER

He prayed with the disciples in the
upper room
Acts 1: 13

He suggested that someone take
Judas' place as a disciple
Acts 1: 15-26

He preached a great sermon at
Pentecost which won three-thousand
people to Christ
Acts 2: 14-40

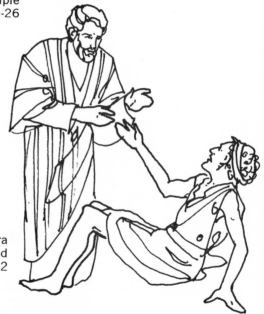

He and John healed a lame beggar at
The Beautiful Gate of the Temple
Acts 3: 1—4: 21

He showed Ananias and Sapphira
how they were lying to God
Acts 5: 1-12

People sat in his shadow so they
could be healed
Acts 5: 15

He refused to obey the Jewish council
when they ordered him to stop
preaching about Jesus
Acts 5: 27-41

He and John put their hands on people
in Samaria, as the Holy Spirit came
into the Samaritans' lives
Acts 8: 14-17

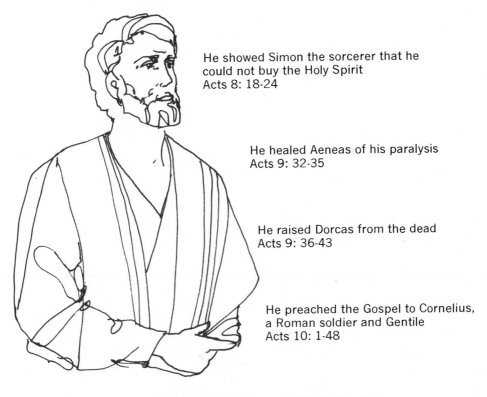

He showed Simon the sorcerer that he
could not buy the Holy Spirit
Acts 8: 18-24

He healed Aeneas of his paralysis
Acts 9: 32-35

He raised Dorcas from the dead
Acts 9: 36-43

He preached the Gospel to Cornelius,
a Roman soldier and Gentile
Acts 10: 1-48

He defended his work with the Gentiles
at a church council in Jerusalem
Acts 11: 1-18

He was released from prison by an
angel
Acts 12: 1-19

He and James helped decide that
Gentiles would not be required to
follow Jewish laws
Acts 15: 1-21

177

*The people were starting
to listen to the apostles more
than the high priest.*

A Beating That Made
Men Happy

The apostles are put in prison

The high priest and his friends were jealous. All the people should be listening to them as the religious leaders. But they weren't. The people were starting to listen to the apostles more than the high priest. Thousands of people were becoming followers of Jesus. Of course, the high priest knew that these people would not obey him if they were following Jesus.

Since they didn't know what else to do, the high priest and his friends had the apostles arrested. They had tried to do this to Peter

and John before, and it didn't work. But they had to stop all this excitement somehow. If they didn't, the whole city of Jerusalem might turn away from them to follow Jesus.

So the high priest and his friends sent the soldiers who guarded the Temple to arrest the apostles. The guards took them and threw them in jail.

But that night something very strange happened. While the city slept, an angel came to visit the apostles in jail.

"Go out of this jail," the angel said. "Get back to the Temple in the morning and preach to the people again."

Go out of jail? The apostles wondered how that could happen. The big doors of the jail were locked. Guards stood outside, too.

But the angel reached toward the doors and opened them. He did not even need a key.

"Go," he whispered.

The apostles hurried from the jail. Surely the guards would stop them at any minute. But the guards didn't even see the apostles as they hurried by. The angel had done something to the guards so they couldn't see.

It was daybreak when the apostles came to the Temple again. Already people were coming to the Temple to pray and think about God. Without waiting, the apostles began to talk to them about Jesus.

The high priest and his friends had no way to know that the apostles were out of jail. So, when morning came, they brought the religious leaders together. They would get everything ready for the apostles' trial.

When things were ready, the high priest sent soldiers to take the apostles out of jail. But the soldiers came hurrying back, full of exciting things to tell the high priest.

"They're gone!" the soldiers shouted. "The prisoners are gone. They've simply disappeared."

"Arrest those guards at the prison," the high priest screamed. "They let the prisoners escape."

"No, no!" said the soldiers. "When we came to the jail, the doors were still locked and the prison guards were in their places. The prisoners disappeared from the jail in the night. But how did they do it?"

The religious leaders began to whisper among themselves. How *did* the apostles do it? They couldn't walk through walls or jail doors. Yet, that must have happened.

Suddenly some other soldiers rushed into the room. They were very excited.

"Go out of this jail," the angel said.
"Get back to the Temple and preach again."

"The prisoners are standing in the Temple, preaching to people again," they said. "What shall we do?"

"Arrest them!" the high priest shouted.

The soldiers did arrest them and brought them before the high priest and the other religious leaders.

"Didn't we tell you not to preach again about Jesus?" the high priest demanded. "You're filling the whole city with your teaching. You're trying to blame us for His death."

Peter looked at the angry high priest. He knew how others hurried to obey the high priest because they were afraid of him. But Peter was not afraid. The Holy Spirit was with him. He wasn't afraid of any man.

"We must obey God, not you," Peter answered. "We have seen Jesus alive after His crucifixion and know that God raised Him from the dead. He can take away the sins of people who ask Him."

182

"You might be fighting God,"
Gamaliel warned the leaders

The high priest and the other religious leaders became very angry when they heard Peter talk like that. Peter was just a Galilean fisherman. But he was trying to tell them about God.

"Kill that man!" some of the religious leaders shouted.

Then a very wise man stood up to speak. Everyone became quiet.

"Shhhh," they said. "Gamaliel wants to say something." The religious leaders all liked Gamaliel because he was so wise.

"Would the soldiers please take the prisoners from the room?" Gamaliel asked. The soldiers hurried to obey. Soon the apostles were gone.

"Men of Israel," said Gamaliel. "You'd better be careful what you're doing. If these men are teaching something wrong, people won't keep on listening to them. But if they're doing what God wants, you might be fighting God. Leave these men alone."

As Gamaliel sat down, the religious leaders began to whisper among themselves. What Gamaliel said made sense. They would do it.

So the high priest called for the prisoners to be brought in again. "Give those men a beating and let them go," he ordered.

Then the high priest screamed at the men, "Don't ever preach about Jesus again."

But the high priest did not know that the beating made the apostles very happy.

"I'm so glad we can suffer some for Jesus," they said. "He suffered so much for us."

Did the apostles quit preaching? No, they didn't. They hurried back to the Temple as fast as they could go. Every day, they kept on preaching and teaching people about Jesus. And many, many of those people became Jesus' followers because the apostles did what God wanted, no matter what men told them to do.

SOMETHING TO THINK ABOUT

1. Why didn't the apostles stop preaching when they were warned to stop? What did Peter tell the high priest?
2. Did the apostles think the things they were saying about Jesus were important? They were willing to risk their lives to tell people about Jesus, weren't they?
3. How important do you think the Gospel is? Is it important enough to tell others? To turn people against you? To make others angry at you? To risk your life for it?
4. Whenever you talk with others about Jesus, ask yourself what the apostles would have done? What would they have done if their friends had made fun of them?
5. What would they have done if they had to work hard to tell people about Jesus? The apostles were willing to do anything for Jesus, weren't they? Are you?
6. The apostles were happy when they could suffer for Jesus. They knew how much Jesus had suffered for them.

184

WHAT THE GOSPELS SAY ABOUT JOHN

He was a son of Zebedee
Matthew 4: 21.

He was a brother of James, the apostle
Matthew 4: 21

His mother was probably Salome, the woman who helped support Jesus during His ministry and brought spices to Jesus' tomb. Salome was probably Jesus' aunt, His mother's sister. So John was Jesus' cousin.
Matthew 27: 56; Mark 15: 40; 16: 1; Luke 8: 3.

He was in the fishing business with his father and brother on the Sea of Galilee
Mark 1: 19, 20.

He was at one time a disciple of John the Baptist
John 1: 35.

He became a disciple of Jesus when John the Baptist told him that Jesus was the Lamb of God
John 1: 35-37.

He left his fishing business when Jesus called him to be a full-time disciple
Matthew 4: 18-22.

He was with Peter and James when Jesus raised Jairus' daughter
Mark 5: 37.

He was with Peter and James when Jesus was transfigured
Mark 9: 2.

His mother tried to get Jesus to promise a place for John and James at His right hand in His kingdom
Mark 10: 35.

He and Peter helped get the Last Supper ready
Luke 22: 8.

He sat next to Jesus at the Last Supper
John 13: 25.

He went with James and Peter to be alone with Jesus while He prayed in the Garden of Gethsemane
Matthew 26: 37.

He went inside the building where Jesus' trial before the high priest was held
John 18: 16.

He was asked to take care of Jesus' mother while he stood beneath Jesus' cross
John 19: 26.

He and Peter went to Jesus' tomb when Jesus rose from the dead
John 20: 2, 3.

Seven Wise Men in Charge of Problems

Seven deacons are chosen

Some of the new disciples were beginning to grumble. It really wasn't too surprising. The group had grown so fast that it was hard for the apostles to keep up with everything. There were only twelve apostles, and there were thousands of new disciples for them to lead.

Peter and the other apostles knew they wouldn't have time to teach and preach if they had to do so many other things. And there were many, many other things to do. Every day someone took food to the poor disciples. Trying to keep them fed was such a big job that some of the poor people didn't get as much as others.

For some reason, the poor people who spoke Greek felt their widows weren't getting as much as those who spoke Hebrew. They didn't mind saying so, too. It was even suggested that the apostles weren't being very fair in this whole matter.

After talking things over, the twelve apostles knew what they must do. They couldn't keep on doing everything themselves. It was too much. Perhaps it was true that some weren't getting their fair share of the food. The twelve apostles couldn't see that every

186

Each day the apostles helped those who needed food and clothing. But if they kept on taking care of people, they wouldn't have time to preach.

one of the thousands of believers was getting what he should. It simply wasn't possible.

Word was sent to all the believers to come to a special meeting. There the apostles would tell what could be done about the problem.

"We must spend our time telling people about Jesus," the apostles told the great crowd of believers. "God doesn't want us to use our time feeding people if we have to quit preaching to do it."

The believers nodded their heads. It was true. The apostles were much too important to go around checking on all these problems. The teaching and preaching would never get done. People wouldn't hear about Jesus.

"Look around you," the apostles went on. "Choose seven wise men who love God. We will put them in charge of the problems. Then we can spend our time preaching and teaching."

The apostles laid their hands
on the seven good men and prayed for them.

It sounded like such a good idea that the believers decided to do it right then and there. But who would the seven best men be?

Somehow everyone seemed to know who to choose. The best always stands out above the rest.

Stephen stood out even above the very best. He was one of those unusual men who seem to be filled with God's Spirit. He was chosen first, then Philip, Prochorus, Nicanor, Timon, Parmenas, and Nicolaus of Antioch.

"Thank God for such wise and good men," the apostles said. "Now God can use them to take charge of the food and other things."

The apostles laid their hands on these seven good men and prayed for them. "Help them and use them," they prayed. "May they always be helpful to You and Your people."

Everyone was happy now. They had seven wonderful men to take care of problems. And they still had the twelve apostles to preach and tell others about Jesus.

189

WHAT THE BIBLE SAYS ABOUT DEACONS

When the Bible speaks of deacons, it is not always talking about the kind of deacons you have in your church. But the duties of a Bible-time deacon may be perfectly right for a deacon today. Read the following, then see what you think.

A Bible-time deacon was a helper. The seven deacons were chosen to help the apostles. The seven were to give out food and help the poor, work which the apostles had been doing. This kind of work had been keeping the apostles from preaching and teaching, which they felt they should be doing.

Even though the deacons were "servants," that did not keep them from also preaching and teaching. Philip was an evangelist and won many to Christ through his evangelistic work (see Acts 6: 2; 8: 4-40). Stephen was a great preacher and miracle-worker (see Acts 6: 8—7: 60).

Romans 16: 1 mentions Phoebe, a woman whom Paul called a "deaconess." She was probably a faithful helper in the church at Cenchreae.

190

WHAT SHOULD A DEACON BE?
I Timothy 3: 8-13

A DEACON SHOULD BE

1. **SERIOUS**—HE DOES HIS WORK WELL

2. **TRUTHFUL**—HE DOESN'T SAY THINGS TWO DIFFERENT WAYS

3. **SOBER**—HE DOESN'T GIVE HIMSELF TO DRINK

4. **UNSELFISH**—HE DOESN'T GIVE HIMSELF TO MONEY

5. **CHRISTIAN**—HE HAS A CLEAR-CUT BELIEF IN CHRIST

6. **PROVED**—HE PROVES HIMSELF IN OTHER CHURCH WORK FIRST

7. **MARRIED TO THE RIGHT PERSON**— HIS WIFE IS THOUGHTFUL, NOT GIVEN TO DRINK, NOT A GOSSIPER, BUT FAITHFUL IN WHAT SHE DOES

8. **REPUTABLE**—HE HAS ONE WIFE ONLY

9. **A GOOD FATHER**—HE MANAGES HIS HOUSE AND CHILDREN WELL

IF A DEACON IS ALL OF THESE THINGS, HE WILL BE RESPECTED AND HE WILL BRING HONOR TO THE LORD

WHAT THE BOOK OF ACTS AND THE EPISTLES SAY ABOUT JOHN

After Jesus ascended into Heaven, John went with the others into the upper room to pray.
Acts 1: 1-14.

One day, when Peter and John went into the Temple, they healed a crippled man.
Acts 3.

Peter and John were arrested and put into prison. But when they were brought before the high council, they spoke boldly, telling the high priest and others that they must obey God rather than men.
Acts 4: 1-22.

When Philip won many to Christ in Samaria, Peter and John went to be with him. Peter and John prayed for these people to receive the Holy Spirit.
Acts 8: 4-25.

John, along with Peter and James, gave Paul "the right hand of fellowship" to preach to the Gentiles.
Galatians 2: 9.

Three Epistles were written by John.
I John, II John, III John.

John was exiled on the Island of Patmos, where God showed him many strange things to come. There he wrote the Book of Revelation.

192